Baby Animals

Baby Animals

Robert Burton

Galley Press

Contents

Previous pages baby grey squirrel, lion cub
This page marsh warbler and chicks

First published in Great Britain in 1976 by
Octopus Books Limited under the title
The Love of Baby Animals

Published in 1988 by Galley Press, an imprint
of W H Smith Limited.
Registered No 237811 England
Trading as W H Smith Distributors
St John's House
East Street
Leicester
LE1 6NE

© 1976 Octopus Books Limited

ISBN 0 86136 053 2

Printed by Mandarin Offset in Hong Kong

Introduction

The object of an animal's existence is to breed, producing replicas of itself which will take its place when it dies. If it does not manage to breed, the animal has been unsuccessful: its life has been pointless. The only exception to this rule is Man, who has the freedom to live as he likes. Yet, for most human beings, having a family still makes life complete, either because bearing and raising a family brings a sense of fulfilment or because of a desire to see one's name and lineage continue. In a way, this is true of animals in that they have to ensure that the species continues and that each animal's attributes are passed on to the next generation.

Human beings have small families and are able to lavish care on each child, but many animals do nothing more than lay huge numbers of eggs. Tapeworms lay several hundred million eggs each year and seashore mussels lay up to 25 million. As with many other 'lower animals', these are simply left to survive as best they can. There is no family life and, once the eggs have been laid, parental duties are finished.

Some animals, however, have taken to nurturing their offspring, and are able to help them over the most difficult period of life until they are able to fend for themselves. The early life of animals and the care they receive from their parents form the subject of this book.

The development of parental care can be seen as advances in a series of steps. From the broadcast scattering of large numbers of eggs comes a reduction in number so that each egg can be given a larger store of yolk to help it develop. Because fewer eggs are laid, a higher proportion must hatch out and the parents often need to guard them against the attacks of predators and also actively help them to develop. Some fishes, such as the sticklebacks and cichlids popular with aquarists, nurture the eggs by fanning them. They blow currents of water over the eggs with their fins to keep them well aerated and prevent the growth of fungi. Other animals retain the eggs inside the body and give birth to live young. Sometimes the eggs simply lie in the oviducts and hatch inside the mother. This method of reproduction is called ovovivipary and occurs in reptiles such as the European viviparous lizard and the slow worm. There is little real difference between egg-laying, or ovipary, and ovovivipary and in ovoviviparous species the eggs are sometimes laid before they hatch. True live birth, or vivipary, involves an intimate connection being made between the maternal tissues and those of the young animal developing inside her, as happens with human babies.

Parental care has its most complete expression in birds and mammals. Birds lay eggs, whereas mammals give birth to live young. The only exceptions are the two monotremes or egg-laying mammals of Australia – the platypus and the echidna. After incubating the eggs in a nest, birds feed their chicks on solid food. Mammals have developed a special feeding mechanism and baby mammals are nourished on their mother's milk. The word mammal comes from the Latin *mamma*, meaning breast, but feeding the young on a special secretion is not unique to mammals. Pigeons feed their nestlings on a 'milk' secreted from the lining of the crop.

The dependence of young mammals on their mother's milk reduces the part that the father can play in their upbringing and, although there are exceptions, the parental role of the male mammal is often minimal. After courtship and mating he usually leaves

the female to bring up the family alone.

In both birds and mammals, there are two basic forms of childhood and parental care. Either the offspring are born helpless and require considerable parental care or they are well advanced and fairly independent. The male is most often brought in to help rear the family if they are born helpless.

Parental care often continues after the young have almost grown up. They are given extra food and protection while they learn to fend for themselves, particularly if the species has a specialized feeding technique. Small woodland birds, such as the tits, spend a few days with their parents after they leave the nest and are fed while they learn to search for insects, but the frigate bird of tropical seas is fed for as long as six months after it has left the nest. Frigate birds catch fish from the surface of the sea without landing and steal fish from other birds as they bring food to their own chicks. Both techniques require

considerable aerobatic skill, which takes time to perfect.

To ensure that parents look after their young, a bond must be formed between them. In most cases the parents have to recognize their young. Mammals usually do this by smell and as soon as the baby is born the mother repeatedly smells it. Birds do not usually recognize their eggs and chicks if they are in the nest, it is only necessary to remember the position of the nest; guillemots, however, lay their eggs straight onto cliff ledges – there is no nest and the parents therefore have to recognize the egg by its markings. Later, they learn to recognize their chick by its calls.

Most animals will not tolerate close contact with their fellows but close contact must be made for mating and parental care to take place. Courtship involves the interplay of signals that draw the sexes together, and similar signals are used to prevent parents from

reacting hostilely towards young animals approaching them. Young birds, such as gull chicks, approach their parents in a submissive posture that allays their aggression, and similar postures are adopted by young mammals. Puppies roll over on their backs, presenting their bellies to their elders. In return the pups are allowed to take liberties with adults, clambering over them and pulling their tails.

Most of the animals portrayed in this book are instantly identifiable to us as babies because they have similar facial characteristics to a human baby. They have rounded faces with large eyes, plump cheeks and prominent foreheads. Perhaps these features which arouse feelings of affection and tenderness in us evoke the same response in adult animals.

Left zebra foal
Above snow goslings

Water Babies

Life on this planet started in the sea and for hundreds of millions of years all animals led a watery existence. Then some animals crept out of the sea and rivers to colonize and exploit the untapped resources of the continents. Some animals still lead a double life. The amphibians live on land but return to water to breed, while the marine turtles, the crocodiles and seals live in water but must return to the land to produce their offspring.

For sea birds such as the auks, albatrosses and penguins, the sea is home and the land is merely a nursery. Breeding on water is difficult for an egg-laying animal when the embryos inside have to breathe air and be kept warm by the parent, and few birds manage to nest on water. Some build island nests, often anchored to water plants, like the moorhen and coot. If the water level rises, they pile more vegetation on the nest to raise the eggs above the flood. These fluffy ducklings (left) are fascinating babies. They become 'imprinted' with their mother and follow her in a little troop.

The water is an even, equable environment. Animals can lay their eggs and leave them to develop and hatch by themselves. Many aquatic invertebrate animals, bristle worms, sea urchins, oysters and the like, lay vast numbers of eggs which they simply shed into the sea, but some have taken to nurturing their offspring. Fewer eggs are laid but, because they are guarded in a nest or attached to the parents' bodies, they are given a better chance of survival.

The eggs of seahorses (above) are very well looked after. They are incubated by the male–not the female–in a special pouch, where they are laid by the female by means of an egg-laying tube. After a month in the pouch, a hundred or so babies are born and are immediately pushed out into the water where they have to fend for themselves.

The marine turtles lead an entirely aquatic existence, peacefully feeding on sea plants or small animals, but they must come ashore to breed. Each year they gather off their breeding beaches, where mating takes place, and the females then come ashore to lay their eggs. Egg-laying behaviour varies somewhat between species. For instance, most species lay their eggs under the cover of darkness but one of the Ridley turtles prefers daylight. However, there is a generalized pattern in the way the females come up the beach, dig a nest and lay their eggs.

The journey up the beach is laborious, and the turtles have to rest at intervals from the effort of dragging their heavy shells. Their destination is the sand above the high-tide line where the eggs will be safe from waves. The first step is to dig a hole. Using its foreflippers, the turtle scrapes away until its whole body is lying in a pit. Then the hindflippers are used alternately to dig a smaller, deeper hole which forms the eggchamber. Into this are laid, on average, 100 round white eggs. When the clutch is complete, the hindflippers are used to fill the pit with sand and, as the turtle moves away, its flailing flippers disguise the exact location of the nest. Each female will return to the beach four or five times during the breeding season to lay more clutches.

The incubation period depends very much on the surrounding temperature, but it usually lasts around two to three months. The entire clutch hatches at once and by scraping with their flippers the baby turtles work their way up through the sand until they lie just beneath the surface. There they wait until the temperature of the sand drops, an indication that the night has fallen. Then they dig themselves free (far right), scuttle down the beach as fast as they can and swim out to sea (bottom left).

A problem that intrigued zoologists was how the baby turtles found their way unerringly to the sea without getting lost inland or foiled by obstacles such as washed-up tree trunks. Eventually they realized that even on dark nights there is a very faint glow over the sea which is discernible even when the water's edge is obscured by sandbanks. The turtles head straight for the glimmer and thus take the shortest route down the beach (right). Even the moon does not put them off course, because its light will be of low intensity compared with the general reflection off the sea.

It is imperative that the baby turtles, which are a fraction of the adult's size (see top left), make this initial journey as quickly as possible and at night. Their shells are soft and thus they have no protection against a host of enemies. The night-time flight protects them from marauding birds but there are plenty of nocturnal predators. Crabs, cats, dogs and snakes hunt along the beach and

sharks and crocodiles are waiting offshore. It has been estimated that, of the 1,800 eggs laid by a green turtle in her lifetime, only 405 emerge as baby turtles, because of nest robbery by dogs, monitor lizards and the like. Of these only 243 reach the sea and after one week at sea a mere 31 still survive, a tiny fraction of the original number.

The 1,800 or so eggs that a turtle lays are sufficient to replenish the stock of adult turtles after all the deductions made by predators, disease and accident. Unfortunately, Man has severely upset this balance by stealing eggs and, worse, killing the females as they come ashore to lay. Over many parts of the turtle's original breeding range, beaches are deserted. Elsewhere they are seriously depleted. This is due partly to the taking of turtles for soup or for 'tortoiseshell' and in addition the rising populations of people living along tropical coasts are eager to supplement their diet with turtle eggs.

In an effort to stem the ebbing current of the turtle's fortunes, farms have been set up where clutches of eggs are dug up and resited within the safety of fenced compounds. The eggs hatch well and the baby turtles are reared to commercial size. In order to restock the number of turtles in the wild, some are only kept until their shells have hardened. Then they are released out to sea so that the huge death rate along the shore is avoided.

The parental care given to baby fishes ranges from simply laying the eggs and leaving them to guarding both the eggs and the babies. Salmon leave their eggs to their fate, but to give them a good start they are laid in a shallow hollow in the gravel bed of a stream – called a 'redd'. The female salmon covers the eggs by scattering gravel over them with vigorous strokes of her tail. The eggs and later the minute fishes, the alevins (below), each with a yolk sac attached, are safe from predators under the gravel. When they have developed enough to brave the outside world, they fight their way towards the light and emerge into a shallow part of the stream, where they can get some protection from being eaten by trout, perch and pike. Here they start to feed on small insect larvae.

By the end of the first year, the baby salmon are about 4 inches (102 mm) long and they are now called 'parr'. They are distinguished by eight to ten oval marks, called parr marks, on the sides of the body, with a red spot between each. The growth of the baby salmon depends on the temperature of the water and the next stage of their lives, when they migrate to the sea, may occur anywhere between the age of one to seven years. The skin develops a silvery layer that covers the parr marks, and the young salmon, now known as 'smolt', migrate downstream. When they reach the sea they eat enormously and grow to 2 feet (610 mm) or more within a year or so. Their name has changed yet again and it is as 'grilse' that they migrate back to their birthplace to breed.

Baby sticklebacks (bottom right) receive constant attention while they are small. As happens with many other fish, such as the seahorse and some of the cichlids, it is the male parent that is most attentive. The male stickleback builds a nest of pondweeds and entices females to lay their eggs in it. Until the eggs hatch five to twelve days later, depending on the water temperature, he stands by the entrance and fans the eggs with his fins. The current of water that streams past aerates them and prevents the growth of moulds. The baby sticklebacks receive similar treatment and when they leave the nest they stay with their father for a while before gathering in schools.

Everyone is familiar with the tadpole (top right), the larva of frogs and toads. These animals are amphibians, a name that means 'double-life' and refers to the land-living adult which has to return to water to breed. The immature larval

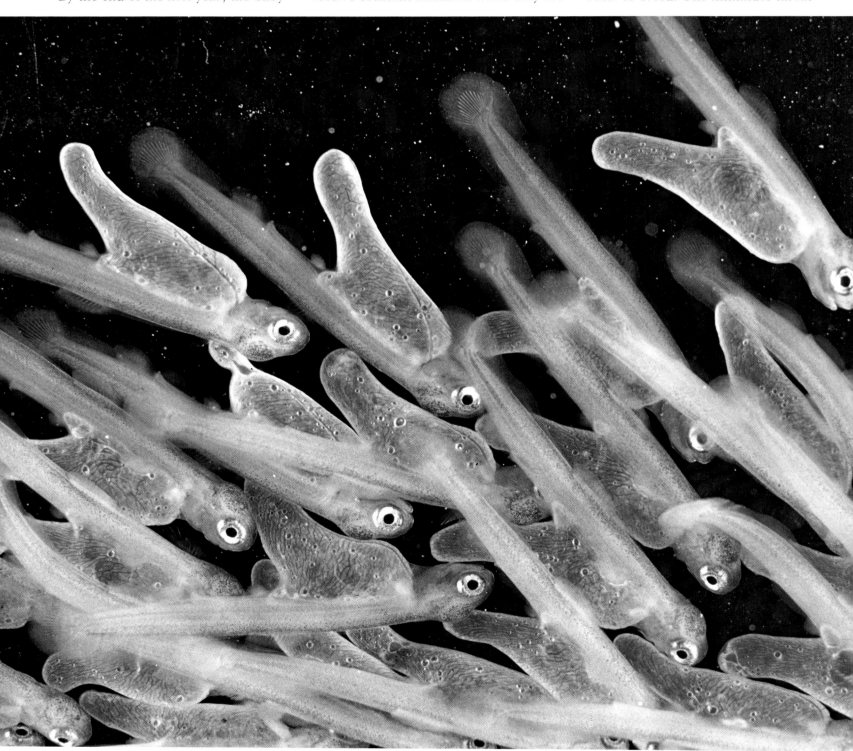

stage can only exist in the water, because, apart from exceptions such as the midwife toad (see page 27), the eggs of amphibians are unable to resist drying up as they lack a protective shell. The jelly surrounding each egg gives some protection and is a defence against predators. It also acts like the glass of a greenhouse, admitting solar radiation which is absorbed by the black egg but preventing warmth escaping, so that the development of the egg is accelerated.

The tadpoles emerge by dissolving the jelly with secretions from special glands. For a time they cling to the remains of the jelly, which still acts as a shield against danger. At this stage, each tadpole has feathery external gills and no legs. It lives on the remains of yolk inside its body until its mouth opens and it can feed on minute organisms. By this time it can swim actively, and the external gills disappear and are replaced by internal gills hidden under a flap of skin, the operculum. The legs grow later – the hindlegs appear to be first to sprout, but in fact the front legs are hidden by the operculum.

The tadpole now begins to take on the appearance of a miniature frog with a long tail. The internal gills are finally replaced by lungs and sometime previously the tadpole will have become carnivorous. It eats water fleas and other small animals, a point not always appreciated by people who keep tadpoles in a jam jar and wonder why they die or eat each other.

The last stage in the transformation of wriggling tadpole into hopping frog is the reabsorption of the tail, which has not always been completed before the froglets come onto land. They gather at the edges of ponds to await propitious conditions, which means a good downpour of rain that soaks the ground and keeps the emerging froglets moist until they can find shelter. A bout of rain after a dry spell may cause a sudden 'explosion' of froglets so that the ground seems to be alive with hopping babies – in the past, when frogs were much more common, a colloquial expression was 'rains of frogs'.

lizards sometimes dig underneath the crocodile as she lies over the nest.

After a four-month incubation, the eggs are ready to hatch. It is now the rainy season and there will be plenty of insects for the baby crocodiles to eat. While they are still in the eggs, the babies begin to grunt, which is the signal for the attentive mother to uncover the nest and allow her brood to climb out. They stay with their mother, following her about like ducklings following a duck. If they get lost they yap until they regain contact. From the start, baby crocodiles are avid feeders, chasing insects in the water or on land.

After a few days, the family disperses but for these vital first few days, the mother crocodile has done a worthwhile

The crocodilians, which include caimans, gharials and alligators as well as the crocodiles, are amphibious reptiles. They are the last survivors of a huge order of reptiles, the Archosauria, to which the dinosaurs belonged. And if we do not act to protect them, pressures of hunting and destruction of swampland may send some of the modern croco- dilians the same way as the dinosaurs.

The difference between the crocodile (right) and the alligator (above) is small. Crocodiles' teeth in the upper and lower jaws are in line, whereas the alligator's upper teeth overhang the lower teeth so that the enlarged fourth lower tooth is hidden when the mouth is shut. In crocodiles, this tooth is visible as it slots into a notch in the upper jaw. The caimans inhabit South America and are distinguished by having bony plates on the belly as well as on the back, an adaptation to life in fast-flowing, boulder- strewn rivers. The gharials or gavials are narrow-snouted crocodiles of the Indian region.

The breeding habits of all crocodilians follow the same pattern and they are among the few reptiles to show any form of parental care. It would be interesting to know whether their dinosaur ancestors

also made good parents; fossil dinosaur eggs have been found in nests and the marine ichthyosaurs gave birth to live young, but behaviour cannot be fossilized and so the question will have to remain unanswered.

The family life of the Nile crocodile shown on the right has been well studied. During the dry season, the female, who has recently mated, starts to build her nest in a shaded place near water. She digs a pit about 2 feet (610 mm) deep, into which she deposits about 90 eggs and covers them up. The estuarine crocodile of South-East Asia and northern Australia builds a mound of leaves rather than digging a pit, and the American alligator mixes mud with rotting vegetation and piles it into a mound 3 foot (915 mm) high. The eggs are laid in this mound and the heat generated by the decomposition of the vegetation incubates them.

The shaded position of the nest is important because the female Nile crocodile stays close by and herself needs protection from the heat of the tropical sun. Guarding the nest is important because there are plenty of nest robbers in search of an easy meal. Yet she is not the best of guardians and monitor job because, unlike the fearsome adults, baby crocodiles have many enemies. Mongooses, herons, eagles and carnivorous fishes are quite capable of capturing a baby crocodile, despite its sharp nip. The most serious threat of all comes from other crocodiles which do not have the slightest compunction about cannibalism. When crocodiles haul themselves out on riverbanks to bask in the sun, they sort themselves into groups of equal size and the smaller ones keep well away from their seniors.

In recent years a more serious threat has hit baby crocodilians, particularly the American alligator of the south-eastern United States. They have become popular as pets, and the pictures on this page show that they are indeed engaging animals. Unfortunately, baby alligators grow up. They are 1 foot (305 mm) long on hatching and grow 10 inches (254 mm) to 1 foot (305 mm) each year, their diet changing from insects and freshwater crustaceans to fish and later to small animals. By this time the baby alligator is a formidable animal and at the age of six years it is mature and ready to breed. The problem is what to do with such an embarrassing pet.

The solution for many people is to dump it, as hundreds of unwanted cats, dogs and other pets are dumped every year when they prove to require more attention than their owners are willing to give. Some alligators are offered to zoos but as this method of disposal becomes choked, more unorthodox methods are used. The result is perennial stories of alligators infesting the sewers of New York, feeding on rats and frightening sewermen, although it is unlikely that they would be able to survive for long.

There are two kinds of beaver (below), the American and the European. Both have been hunted extensively for their skins but, encouragingly, both are now recovering their numbers under protection. Beavers are remarkable civil engineers – they build 'lodges' in the centre of a lake, which may itself be artificially created by building huge dams across rivers. They are also unusual among mammals in that they are monogamous and apparently mate for life.

Each lodge is the home of a beaver family, which consists of two parents and two litters of young. Birth takes place in May and on average there are three kits in a litter. Their birth is the signal for most animals, certainly for other rodents, this is the time when the family normally breaks up, but the young beavers stay with their parents. They help with the day-to-day activities of a beaver family, felling trees for maintenance of the dams and lodge and collecting branches of willow and poplar whose bark forms the main winter diet. At first the young beavers are likely to be more of a hindrance than a help, but gradually they acquire the skills of felling and moving timber and heavy construction. These skills are, in fact, instinctive but most instinctive behaviour requires a certain amount of practice for it to reach perfection.

Otters (right) are carnivores related contains usually two or three cubs, sometimes more. At first the cubs are blind and toothless, but they already have a fine coat of dark, silky hair. Their eyes open in about five weeks and three weeks later they leave the nest with their mother. The dog otter lives separately and takes little notice of his young family.

The otter cub is born with the instinct to swim, but it is very hesitant about its first entry into the water and its mother may have to take the initiative by pushing it in. Once in, the cub starts swimming confidently, although when it it still very young it may take rides on its mother's back. Learning to catch fish will, however, take considerable

the father and the young of the previous year to temporarily abandon the lodge, leaving the mother in sole charge. The new kits are born fully furred and with their eyes open, so they are active almost immediately. The lodge cannot contain them and they are soon exploring the submerged entrance hole and the ventilation holes. To retrieve them, the female beaver carries them clasped between her chin and arms while she walks on her hind legs. When the kits are a few days old, the mother brings them tender leaves to eat and complete weaning follows soon after, the young beavers eating the same food as the adults.

As the young beavers become more active and start to wander from the lodge, their father is readmitted. For to the weasels and badgers. They hunt in rivers and lakes and sometimes live on rocky sea coasts. With their streamlined bodies and waterproof fur, they are at home in water and they swim by rhythmic undulations of the body and muscular tail. Their feet are webbed and help them to manoeuvre when they are chasing fish.

Otters are most elusive animals, partly because they are very shy and also because they are nomadic, rarely staying long in one place. As a result their private lives are rather a mystery. We know that cubs may be born at any time of the year, although mainly in spring, and that they are born in a nest lined with grasses and rushes in a hole in a river bank or on the surface of the water deep in a reed bed. The litter practice. When they are travelling, the family swims in line astern formation, the cubs following faithfully behind the mother.

The family stays together over the winter and breaks up when the mother is ready to mate again. During this time, the cubs learn to chase fish and hunt for small animals under stones along the banks, but they also have plenty of time for playing. The whole family is sometimes seen tumbling together on the ground, their long flexible bodies entwining, and tobogganing on a muddy or snow-covered slope is a favourite otter pastime.

The seals fall into two natural groups.
There are the true or hair seals, of which
the grey seal and common seal are
examples, and the fur seals, sealions and
the walrus, which are sometimes called
eared seals. The eared seals have small
external ears, as can be seen on the fur
seals shown here (bottom right), but the
true seals have a bare ear opening,
which shows clearly on the head of the
common seal (far right). A more
obvious distinction is the arrangement
of the hindflippers. Eared seals can turn
their hindflippers forward, lift up their
bodies and bound over the ground. True
seals cannot do this; they are clumsy on
land and can only hitch themselves
along on their bellies. They use their
hindflippers for swimming, whereas
the eared seals swim with their foreflippers.

Both kinds of seals spend their lives at
sea feeding on fish and other marine
animals, but once a year they come to
land to breed, often in large colonies
numbering hundreds or thousands. The
only seals that do not come on land are
the Arctic and Antarctic seals which
bear their pups on the surface of the
frozen sea.

The baby seals have to spend a
certain time on land or on the ice until
they have developed sufficiently to be
able to swim strongly. Their babyhood is
usually very short. Grey seals of the
North Atlantic (top right) are born with
a white coat and at birth they are very
thin, but the cows feed them on fat rich
milk so that they put on weight very
rapidly and at the end of three weeks are
fully weaned. The cows lose interest in
them after this but by now the pups
have a thick layer of blubber which will
sustain them while they shed their white
pup coat and put to sea in search of
their own food.

The common seal (far right) of the
North Atlantic and North Pacific is born
in a more advanced condition than other
seals. The white pup coat is shed before
birth and the pup emerges with its adult
coat. Its advanced condition is essential
because the pup is born on a sandbank
or a weed-covered rock at low water,
and it must be able to swim well when
its birth site is covered by the rising tide.
At first the pup does little more than
float, but in a couple of days it can dive
quite well. Sometimes it rides on its
mother's back and if danger threatens
she may force it to dive by pushing it
under with a flipper.

The female true seal does not need to
feed during the short suckling period,
but the eared seals have evolved a
different maternal system. Suckling in
these species lasts for three months, and
after the first week the cows abandon
their black-coated pups at intervals and
swim out to sea to feed. Meanwhile the
pups spend their time sleeping with their
flippers wrapped around their bodies
for warmth or wandering around the

beach. Later, they become more adventurous and run around in groups, chasing gulls, mock-fighting and investigating anything that catches their interest.

When a cow arrives back at the shore after feeding, she has to find her pup among the hundreds that litter the beach. As a first step, she returns to the place where she left it and calls loudly. Similarly, when hungry, the pup makes its way to the spot where it was last fed. The pup recognizes its mother's voice, calls back and comes towards her, but so will other pups that are hungry and are waiting for their mothers. The cow has to decide which pup is hers, which she does by smell. Recognition is very important as the cow feeds only her own pup. The process of identification and recognition starts at birth when the cow and pup exchange calls in a bleating duet and the cow repeatedly sniffs the pup.

Once identification is made, the cow turns on her side to suckle the pup. Like the grey seal pup, it is treated to a meal of very rich milk. During the two days

that the cow spends ashore at each visit, the pups put on weight enormously, perhaps as much as a 30 per cent increase. Its weight will drop again during the cow's week-long feeding expeditions, but there is a general upward trend until weaning. A newly fed pup can be recognized immediately by its distended belly, which almost scrapes the ground as it waddles along.

Babies from Eggs

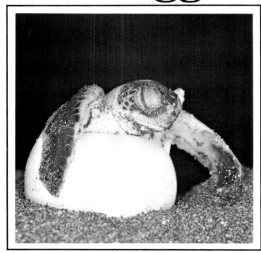

The overwhelming majority of fishes and reptiles, as well as all the amphibians and birds, lay eggs. Some, like the common frogs and toads, abandon them to develop on their own – large numbers of eggs are laid but large numbers perish before they hatch or before the young animals grow up. Other species have taken to caring for their eggs and babies. They build a nest so that the eggs are kept together in one place, making parental care much easier. Care is most important for birds, which are warm-blooded – their eggs must be kept at nearly body temperature throughout the whole period of development.

In some egg-laying species, the eggs are abandoned after being laid in a nest which gives them protection from enemies. The turtles shown on pages 10–11 bury their eggs which hatch out by themselves several weeks later (see above). The only birds to abandon their eggs after they are laid are some of the megapodes or incubator birds of Australia and Malaysia. One species of jungle fowl lays its eggs in sand, leaving the sun to keep them warm. All other birds, however, use their body heat to keep their eggs warm. Except for the cormorants and gannets which wrap their webbed feet around the eggs and the jacana which holds its eggs under its wings, the eggs are kept warm against the 'incubation patch', an area of the breast which loses its feathers during the breeding season and acts as a hotwater bottle.

Once the eggs hatch, the chicks may be born blind and naked or they may have a coat of fine down and be active enough to leave the nest within a short space of time. The former are known as altricial or nidicolous young, while the latter are precocial or nidifugous.

The spotted flycatcher (left) is a typical altricial bird. It is seen here with nestlings which are nearly ready to fly, but the parents still have to drop food into their gaping mouths.

The American robin (right), a cousin of the European robin, raises two, sometimes three, families a year, as it is one of the first birds to lay eggs in the spring and has a long nesting season. The female robin plays the major role in raising the family. She builds the nest, which has a soft grass lining on a thin plastering of mud, in one day's activity. The male helps bring material but otherwise shows little interest. He leaves his mate to incubate the three or four eggs but sometimes helps to feed the chicks.

Altricial nestlings, those which stay in the nest until ready to fly, have an instinctive pattern of behaviour to ensure that their parents feed them. When they are hungry, they open their bills to display the brightly coloured lining of the mouth, red in some species, yellow in the American robin. The colour acts as an irresistible stimulus for the parent bird to drop food into the mouth and the nestling continues to gape until it is full.

Even when hungry, the nestlings gape only when the parent bird arrives at the nest. When they are still very young, they sense the parent's arrival by the sudden movements of the nest. The nestlings immediately rear up, stretching their necks vertically with mouths agape. Once their eyes have opened, movements of the nest are no longer a sufficient stimulus and the chicks react only to the sight of the parent. The gape is still directed upwards, like the American robins here, and only later do the chicks start to direct the gape at the parent, like the nestling spotted flycatchers on the previous page.

An important difference between the nesting habits of small songbirds like the American robin and birds of prey like the African wood owl (bottom left) and Verreaux's eagle (bottom right) is that a clutch of songbird eggs hatch together, meaning that the nestlings leave the nest together, while in birds of prey the hatching is staggered. This is a survival mechanism designed to cope with the predatory bird's erratic food supply. If there are plenty of small animals to feed to the nestlings, all will thrive to be launched on an independent life. But frequently prey is scarce and the parents cannot bring enough food for all the nestlings. If all hatched at once, none of them would get sufficient food for their full development. Staggered hatching means that some nestlings get a head start; they seize food from their younger siblings and, if food is short, the latter die. Thus the older nestlings thrive at the younger's expense.

Only the female bird of prey incubates the eggs. She is normally dependent on food brought by her mate but, if food is short, she may have to leave the nest to do her own hunting. Meanwhile the eggs are vulnerable to marauding crows and other egg-stealers.

Small songbirds continue to be fed for some time after they have left the nest, while they learn to find their own food. Birds of prey are dependent on their parents for much longer as they have to learn the skilled techniques of hunting. Young tawny owls, for instance, leave the nest in May and are cared for by their parents for another three months. By this time they must be adept hunters because they are then driven from their parents' territory and left to find all their own food. They have to choose a hunting territory which is not already claimed by another tawny owl and unfamiliarity with the new territory makes hunting doubly difficult.

If it seems that the early life of a bird of prey is fraught with disaster, we must remember that all these dangers are a

natural way of preventing over-population. If there is plenty of food, many young will survive, but famine leads to an automatic cutback in reproduction.

Unlike the other birds shown here, the Canada goslings (overleaf) are precocial babies, which means they are ready to leave the nest as soon as they hatch out. The parent geese therefore do not have to cope with the problem of bringing them food and at a very early age the goslings are able to fend for themselves. But they still need protection from predators, and to prevent them wandering off on their own both goslings and ducklings are 'imprinted' on their mother so that they instinctively follow her everywhere she goes.

Amphibians and reptiles are cold-blooded, so they do not need to keep their eggs or babies warm like the birds and mammals. Some just lay their eggs and leave them, but a few care for their offspring, although none go so far as birds and mammals in feeding their babies.

Although maternal solicitude is rare in reptiles, some amphibians have evolved strange forms of parental care. The midwife toad of Western Europe (below right) is so named because the male appears to help the female lay her eggs. He manipulates her cloaca with his feet for about 20 minutes before spawning, presumably as a stimulus to make her

lay. When ready, she stretches out her hindlegs and extrudes her eggs onto them. Spawning takes place on land and the male urinates onto the eggs to make the surrounding jelly swell up. Then he wraps the string of eggs around his legs and walks away with them. For the next three weeks he carries the eggs as he searches for food and on dry nights he goes to water to moisten them. Eventually, he enters the water where the tadpoles hatch out.

Another strange amphibian is the marsupial frog, which is a kind of South American tree frog. As it lives in trees it is inconvenient to have to come down to water to breed and special provision is

made for carrying the eggs in a pouch on the back of the female frog. She lays less than fifty eggs, but each is large and very rich in yolk so that there is plenty of food for development.

When marsupial frogs mate, the male climbs on the female's back and the female straightens her hindlegs so that her back is tilted sharply downwards and the eggs roll into the entrance of the pouch. On the way they are fertilized by the male. When the tadpoles are ready to merge, the female climbs down her tree and enters water. There she hooks a hindleg over her back and pulls back the mouth of the pouch to let the tadpoles out. She seems to know when an egg is

about to hatch and release the tadpole, and pulls back the correct side of the pouch entrance with the appropriate left or right hindleg.

The most common form of parental care among reptiles is ovovivipary, the retention of the eggs inside the mother's body until they hatch. The European slow-worm is an exponent of this means of reproduction. Not a worm, nor even a snake, the slow-worm is a legless lizard – it is quite a common trait for lizards to lose their legs and adopt a serpentine habit. The baby slow-worms develop in the egg capsule which is enclosed by a thin transparent membrane rather than a leathery shell. Sometimes the hatching

process is delayed until the egg is laid and the baby slow-worms can be seen curled up inside (below left).

The advantage of ovoviviparity is that the developing eggs benefit from the parent's efforts to keep warm. Although cold-blooded, many reptiles regulate their body temperature to some degree by basking in the sun and sheltering under stones or vegetation in cold weather. The developing eggs in an ovoviviparous species will, therefore, be kept at a higher temperature than if they were left in a nest, and they consequently develop more quickly.

In very cold regions, ovoviviparous species have a natural advantage. The

European adder lives in Finland and Scandinavia beyond the Arctic Circle, where the summer is short and cool. It can also breed nearly 10,000 feet (3,000 metres) up in the Swiss Alps. Its North American equivalent is the common garter snake, which reaches as far north as Labrador and the Yukon.

None of these reptiles show any parental care after giving birth, although young adders seem to stay near their mothers for a while. There is an old story that the adder swallows her young when danger threatens – this probably arose from people with little knowledge of anatomy killing an adder and finding the unborn young in the oviduct.

Babies in Nests

Many of the most familiar animals bear their babies in nests of soft materials such as grass and dead leaves, which are usually lined with fur stripped from the mother's belly. These animals include the rodents, such as rats, mice, voles and squirrels, and the rabbits, hares and guinea pigs.

Most of these babies are born in an early stage of development and are as helpless as a human baby. They have no fur and rely on their mother's body heat and the thick lining of the nest to keep warm. There are, however, exceptions to the rule of naked and helpless at birth among these animals. As we shall see, hares and guinea pigs are born with a coat of fur and are fairly active at birth.

Being a mother to a litter of helpless babies in a nest is a full-time business, but there are advantages in having helpless babies. A baby born at an early stage of development spends less time in its mother's body and is very small at birth. Consequently many babies can be born in one litter, such as the eight edible dormice babies (left). They are born only three weeks after mating and growth is then very rapid. Baby hedgehogs (above) double in weight in their first week and after seven weeks they are ten times as heavy as when they were born. Luckily for the mother hedgehog, the babies are born without spines, but the first coat of soft spines appears in a few hours. Unlike the adults, baby hedgehogs cannot roll up until about eleven days after birth.

Because of their large litters these animals can breed very quickly. Dormice only produce one or two litters a year but mice, voles and rabbits are very prolific and some voles have as many as five or six litters every year, each of about six babies.

Plagues of lemmings, voles and sometimes mice do occur on occasions, but usually the population is kept down by the many hunting animals which prey on them.

The old English name for a rabbit was 'coney'. Rabbits were brought to Britain by the Normans who kept them on farms called 'warrens'. At first only baby rabbits (below left) were called 'rabbits' but gradually the name came to be used for the adults. Newly born rabbits are blind, deaf and almost naked and rely on their mother, the doe, for warmth and protection. They are born in a nest, usually at the end of a short burrow called a 'stop' or 'stob' but sometimes on the surface of the ground. The doe visits the stop once a day to suckle the babies. Their eyes open at eleven days and after two weeks they leave the nest and start to eat solid food.

The cottontail rabbit of America always nests on the surface. So named because the white tail resembles a cotton boll, the cottontail doe bears about seven babies (above left), each weighing only 1 ounce (28·3 grams). The nest is a hollow scraped in the ground and lined with dry grass and soft fur from the doe's belly. It is so small that the doe has to suckle her young by crouching over them.

Hares differ from rabbits in their long hindlegs and their long black-tipped ears. A baby brown hare or leveret (right) is born in a much more advanced state than a rabbit. Its eyes are already open and it has a short coat of fur. The family is born in the mother's resting place or 'form', a depression in the grass of an open field, often among gorse or brambles. Within a very short time each leveret leaves the mother's form and makes its own nearby.

This leveret is cleaning its fur, an important job for all animals. If the fur gets dirty and matted, it loses its waterproofing and no longer keeps the animal warm. Baby animals must, therefore, learn to groom themselves at a very early age. Some babies are kept clean by their mother, who also keeps the nest clean. Washing is not only hygienic, the licking is also good for the baby's general health; if baby rats are handled and petted frequently, they grow up healthier and better able to cope with adverse conditions of cold or starvation. Grooming is also pleasurable and animals regularly groom each other as a sign of friendship.

Mice and voles are very similar animals, and to many people there is no difference between them. Indeed, the word 'vole' is short for 'voldmouse' which merely means field mouse. Naturalists distinguish them by the cheek teeth, which in most voles continue to grow throughout life. In other rodents, only the incisor teeth, which are used for gnawing, grow continually. There are also differences in outward appearance. Voles have blunt noses and short tails, and their ears and eyes are small and almost hidden in the long dense fur.

The field vole or short-tailed vole, (below) once known as the grass mouse, is an inhabitant of meadows and pastures but it is also found on moors and in open woodlands, and it regularly comes into gardens. The nest is usually constructed under a tuft of long, coarse grass and is covered with a dome of grass stems that have been shredded longitudinally and worked into a thick felt. So carefully made is the nest that it is extremely difficult to find a vole's nest except by accident; there is little to distinguish it from the surrounding dead grass. The female vole enters and leaves at any point in the nest as there is no proper entrance.

An easier way of finding vole nests is to turn up logs or sheets of corrugated iron lying on the ground. If one is lucky, an open cup-shaped nest will be found. The vole will shoot away and disappear into the grass but there may be some babies left in the nest. At birth, they are blind, naked and quite helpless. All they can do is squirm around in search of the warmth of their mother who has deserted them. She will soon return, however, but, as happens with many animals, the disturbance makes her abandon the nest.

There may be five to seven baby voles in a litter. They are weaned when they are fourteen to eighteen days old. The family shown below are almost ready to leave their mother. They are already nibbling solid food and in a week or two they will be mature and ready to start their own families. As one field vole may have a dozen litters a year, field voles are very numerous and they form the staple diet of many hunting animals, including weasels, foxes, owls and hawks.

Wood mice or long-tailed field mice (right) are found in both woods and fields. They sometimes come into houses, particularly in winter, and may be mistaken for house mice. These babies are almost fully grown but their ears are not as erect as those of an adult. The childhood of mice is very like that of voles. They are born in a nest of grass that may be in a burrow or under a pile of fallen twigs and leaves. Sometimes, when the female is disturbed in the nest, she runs away with the babies clinging to her teats. They run in step and, if she has to jump, they grip tight and are carried with her. A more remarkable way of transporting the family safely is the shrew's 'caravan'. When a shrew is out with her nearly full-grown babies and they are alarmed by a noise or a slight shower of rain, they run behind their mother and form up in a line. The first grabs the fur at the base of her tail, the next fastens itself in the same way to the first, and so on until all are secure in single file. Sometimes two lines form. Then they all move off, keeping in step and leaping obstacles together like a miniature train winding through the undergrowth.

The familiar squirrels are rodents. They have sharp claws for clinging and feathery tails which help them to balance, particularly when leaping from tree to tree. Unlike most rodents, their eyesight is very good and is very important for judging distances from one branch to another. Not all squirrels live in trees, however – there are many kinds of ground squirrels, for example the marmots, chipmunks and prairie dogs.

It is sometimes said that the grey squirrel (right) is not a true squirrel but a 'tree rat'. This is quite untrue. The grey squirrel of the United States was introduced to the British Isles, where its habits are very similar to those of the native red squirrel. Squirrels make two kinds of nest but only the winter 'drey', a dome of leafy twigs set in the angle of trunk and branch, is used as a nursery. It is lined with leaves, moss, grass and often with strips of honeysuckle bark if this is available. An old crow's nest may be used as the foundations of a nest and the nursery drey is sometimes built in a hollow tree. Two litters of young are born each year, the first arriving in late winter. Like all babies which spend the first weeks of life in a nest, young squirrels are blind, naked and helpless.

By the time the young squirrel leaves the drey, it has grown a short coat of

fur. It can be immediately distinguished as a youngster by its slender tail, which takes some time to reach full adult bushiness. The young red squirrel, squatting on the branch (above left) also lacks the characteristic ear tufts of the adults but its whiskers are already well grown, as are its claws.

At first, the squirrel is very cautious as it climbs along branches and keeps a good grip with its sharp claws. It has a natural instinct to grip tightly, as anyone who has reared a squirrel will know – if it climbs up your arm, it is extremely difficult to dislodge. The hind feet are turned so that the toes are directed backwards and the claws can support the squirrel when it is coming down a tree trunk. The tail is also kept pressed firmly against the trunk to give it extra support and grip.

The movements of a young squirrel are very jerky – a few rapid paces, then a pause. There is none of the lithe agility of the adult. When it comes to make a jump, it hesitates and baulks at any gap over a few inches. With each day the young squirrel gains confidence and by the time it is weaned it can jump several feet. If it does miss its footing it recovers in a flash, throwing out its feet with claws extended to get a temporary hold. Then the legs and tail are used to get a firm enough grip for the squirrel to haul itself back up onto the branch.

Agility must be acquired by weaning because the squirrel now has to clamber through the foliage in search of food. A young squirrel's education includes learning how to find food as well as how to climb. If it is lucky it finds food that is ready to eat, like the open coconut that has attracted the African bush squirrel (below left). After chewing off a piece of coconut flesh, the squirrel holds it in its forepaws while nibbling. Nutshells pose a problem. All squirrels open nuts in the same way, but young squirrels have to practise the technique. When first faced with a nut the squirrel gnaws at it in a most untidy manner, but with practice it learns to gnaw a small hole in the top, insert its teeth and twist so that the shell splits neatly in two halves.

Two of the most popular pets for children are the golden hamster and the guinea pig. They are extremely easy to keep and, apart from their prolific breeding, the only disadvantage is that golden hamsters are nocturnal and can usually only be seen in the evening.

Although these animals are similar in appearance, they are not closely related. The golden hamster (below left) is related to the voles but not much is known about its habits in the wild. All golden hamsters, which must number many thousands, are descended from one family. In 1930, a single female and her twelve young were dug out of their burrow near Aleppo, in Syria.

They were taken to the Hebrew University, Jerusalem, where it was found that they were very easy to keep and could be used for scientific research into the mechanism of hibernation.

Hamsters hibernate during the winter, although they wake up every now and then for a feed from their store of seeds and vegetables. Hamster food stores are so large that in some places they become agricultural pests.

Hamsters are solitary and the male has to be taken from the female after mating. Gestation is extremely short, the naked helpless young being born after fifteen days. There may be as many as twenty in one litter and when they are

weaned three or four weeks later, they immediately leave the protection of their mother's nest.

Guinea pigs come from South America where they were domesticated by the Incas from the wild Brazilian cavy. There are now three main varieties. The ordinary English short-haired guinea pig is the most like the wild cavy; the Peruvian variety has long soft hair, and these Abyssinian rough-haired guinea pigs (bottom right) have their hair arranged in rosettes, just as if they had been through a hedge backwards. The family life of guinea pigs is very different from that of hamsters and their relatives the voles. Instead of being born about

fifteen days after conception, they are retained in the mother's body for nine weeks. The size of the litter is also smaller, between one and four young. The long gestation means that the babies are born in a more advanced state, fully furred and able to run after only a few hours. When only one day old they start to nibble solid food, but they are not properly weaned for three weeks.

The dormouse was a popular pet with English children before it became rare and before imported guinea pigs and hamsters became common. It must have been even less sociable a pet than the hamster: not only are dormice nocturnal, they are proverbial for being heavy sleepers. The dormice shown on page 28 are fat or edible dormice which, as their name suggests, were specially bred for the table in Roman times. The nest is made in a hollow tree and the babies must become independent soon enough to feed and put on weight before they hibernate.

In recent years a new pet has become popular. This is the gerbil or sand rat (below right), an inhabitant of desert and semi-desert regions of Africa and Asia. There are many kinds of gerbil and some have been studied for insight into the mechanisms that allow them to survive in drought conditions. From the laboratory they have been introduced into the home where they make attractive, easily kept pets.

In the wild, gerbils live in burrows and most kinds are active at night, as is shown by their big eyes. They feed on leaves, flowers, seeds and roots, and they store food in their burrows to tide them over the dry season. In Iraq, their stores are raided by hamsters.

Gerbils can raise several litters of one to eight young during the rainy season. The babies stay underground for three weeks, then they cautiously come to the surface. By this time they are miniatures of the adult, like this young gerbil sniffing noses with its mother in greeting.

Living Cradles

A problem for any animal that bears small, helpless young is the question of mobility. The babies can be left in the nest while the mother goes feeding, but sometimes there comes a time when the babies have to be moved, perhaps because the nest has been disturbed or because one of them has strayed and must be retrieved. A female hoary marmot (above), a heavily built ground squirrel which lives in the Rocky Mountain region, is shown here carrying one of her babies to a new den.

Carrying the baby is even more important when the parents are active and there is no proper nest. Primates, such as the chimpanzee, carry their babies clasped to the breast or riding pick-a-back. The problem of carrying babies is intensified in those animals which fly or glide.

The flying lemur (left) is perhaps better described by its alternative name of 'colugo', as it is not a lemur and does not fly! It glides from tree to tree in the South-East Asian forests and the mother carries her single young hanging tight to her teats or fur with its teeth and claws.

The group of mammals which have specialized in carrying their babies is the marsupials. These animals, of which the kangaroo is probably the best-known example, carry their babies in pouches. Australia is the main home of the marsupials and a wide variety of forms has evolved there.

The pouch, or marsupium, can be thought of as a second womb. Baby marsupials are born after a very short gestation, only twelve days for bandicoots and opossums. They are still tiny and not properly formed when they make their way to the pouch and attach themselves to the teats, where development is completed. When they have reached the stage that a placental mammal has already completed at birth, baby marsupials are detached from the teat, although they remain in the pouch for some time.

The koala or koala bear (below), known affectionately and not without reason as the Australian teddy bear, is a sluggish tree-climbing marsupial. It eats little else but eucalyptus or gum tree leaves, and as the Australian forests are cleared the inoffensive koala is gradually becoming rarer.

The koala's decline is not helped by its slow breeding rate. Pregnancy is short, as is usual in marsupials, and the single baby is born in four or five weeks. It makes its way to the rear-facing pouch and, from a birth weight of 1/5 ounce (5.3 grams), it increases to 1 pound (454 grams) in four months. It is now ready to leave the pouch, but as its mother rarely comes to the ground, it cannot run about like other babies. Instead it climbs onto its mother's back and clings tightly to her fur. Pictures like this of a mother koala carrying her identical but smaller baby, each with its tufted ears, 'button' snout and contented expression have helped to make the koala such a popular animal.

The baby koala spends a further six months on its mother's back, by which time it is at least one third of her size. This would, no doubt, prove a great strain if it were not for the slow leisurely habits of the species. For a while, the baby continues to return to the pouch to obtain milk, and the mother also feeds it on a green slime of semi-digested food that has passed through her digestive tract. This less charming habit rather taints the koala's appeal and is rarely mentioned! It starts before the baby leaves the pouch and continues for about one month. The importance of the slime is probably to pass to the baby's digestive system the bacteria that are essential in helping to digest the tough eucalyptus leaves.

The opossums (left) are a group of American marsupials numbering about sixty species. Most live in South America but the Virginia opossum is widespread in the United States, Central America and south-west Canada. Opossums look rather like rats and range in size from a mouse to a domestic cat. The usual haunt of the Virginia opossum is on the

ground but it climbs readily if chased and sometimes looks for food in trees. Its naked tail is prehensile and acts as an extra limb. Other opossums spend more time in the trees.

The gestation period lasts twelve to thirteen days and large litters of babies, numbering eight to 25, are born in rapid succession. Each makes its way to the teats in the slit-like pouch on the mother's belly but, as there are only seven to seventeen teats available, some of the babies are doomed from the start. Some of the South American opossums such as the mouse opossum lack a pouch and the babies are exposed as they cling to the mother's underside. They are perfectly safe as the mother opossum moves about, because newly born marsupials are attached very firmly to the teat. The tip of the teat swells inside the baby's mouth so that it cannot let go.

The young spend ten to eleven weeks in the pouch before they first come out. After this they sleep in the nest but accompany the mother when she goes foraging. The entire family climbs onto the mother's back and clings firmly to her fur. As they grow older, they almost swamp her and if the family is large, movement must become very difficult for her.

The baby opossums hang on with their toes and wrap their tails around the nearest convenient part of the mother's body. This gave rise to the idea that the mother opossum holds her tail over her back and the babies wrap their tails around hers as if 'straphanging' on a bus. This delightful notion was disproved, however, as recently as twenty years ago.

The Virginia opossum is responsible for the well-known phrase 'playing possum'. When an opossum is threatened it lies perfectly still, with its hair dishevelled and tongue lolling. To all appearances it is dead. Many predators will not eat carrion, so they leave the 'dead' opossum alone and go away. A few minutes later, it miraculously recovers and runs off. How soon baby opossums learn the trick is not recorded but it would be no good if the mother played 'possum' while the babies continued to squirm.

The kangaroo (below right) bounding over the Australian outback and carrying its baby in its pouch, is for most people the best known of all the marsupials. It is from studies of kangaroos that we have learned the mysteries of pouch birth. The first description of a kangaroo birth was made in 1830 but zoologists remained sceptical until 1923 when a birth was watched at New York Zoological Gardens.

Shortly before birth, the female kangaroo cleans out her pouch, holding it open with her forepaws and licking inside. Then she takes up the birth position, sitting on the base of the tail which is passed forward between her legs. The infant kangaroo is only $\frac{3}{4}$ inch

(19 mm) long! It is blind and almost helpless but its forelegs, which are small in the adult, are very strong. Using its claws to get a purchase, it drags itself through its mother's fur to the pouch, a journey which takes three minutes. At first zoologists could not believe that such a tiny scrap of an animal could find its way to the pouch unaided and they decided that the mother must move it with her lips or forepaws, but a film of kangaroo birth has set aside all doubts. Somehow, presumably using its sense of smell, the baby finds its own way.

Once in the pouch, some time is spent finding the teat, but once there the baby clings to it for six to seven months. By this age it is ready for short journeys in the open, but whenever danger threatens the young kangaroo or 'joey' leaps back into the pouch head first, then turns a rapid somersault so that its head sticks out. As the 'joey' grows it spends increasingly more time outside the pouch until eventually it is too big to get in. Its mother will actively prevent it from trying to enter the pouch as there may already be a new baby growing inside.

One of the disadvantages of pouch birth is having to carry the extra weight of a baby, and it is sad to relate that kangaroos sometimes eject their young when hard chased.

Kangaroos, the smaller wallabies, koalas and the American opossums are all well known, but there are many other less familiar marsupials. The rabbit bandicoot or bilby (bottom left) is a prodigious burrower, boring its way into the earth in search of insects. As with most quadrupedal marsupials, its pouch opens backwards. There are also marsupial mice, like the fat-tailed dunnart (below left). Some marsupial mice have a pouch that opens backwards or one that is no more than a fold of fur. When the large litter leaves the pouch they are carried on their mother's back, like the opossums, all literally hanging on for dear life.

The spotted cuscus (top right) is one of
the Australian opossums of the phalanger
family, not to be confused with the
American opossums shown on page 41
which belong to a different family of
marsupials. It looks and behaves rather
like a monkey because it lives in trees
and uses its long tail as an extra limb
to grip branches. The spotted cuscus,
one of several species, is found in New
Guinea and, like so many forest-
dwelling animals of the region, very
little is known of its habits. All we know
about its family life is that cuscuses must
breed all the year round, because it is
very unusual to find a female without
a baby in its pouch.

The dozen or more ringtail possums
(far right) are also members of the
phalanger family. They got their name
because they carry their tail coiled in a
tight ring. They are agile tree-dwellers
and their range spreads from New
Guinea down the eastern coast of
Australia to Tasmania. Their breeding
habits do not differ from those of other
marsupials, as far as is known.
Unlike the quadrupedal ground-living
marsupials such as the bandicoots and
marsupial mice shown on the previous
pages, the phalangers have a pouch that
opens forwards. Like the jumping
kangaroos, their way of life makes this
arrangement essential to prevent the
babies shaking out. However, there is an
exception: the koala, although it is a
kind of phalanger, has a rear-facing
pouch. Living as it does in trees there
must be a danger of the newborn koala
baby losing its hold and falling on its
way to the pouch, but their grip is
extremely tenacious and, anyway, with
a gestation of only two to three weeks
a replacement is soon on its way in the
event of an accident.

The tree kangaroo (bottom right) is
another tree-dwelling marsupial that
needs to be careful of dropping its
baby. It lives in the rain forests of
Australia and New Guinea and is very
similar to ordinary, ground-living
kangaroos in appearance. Surprisingly,
for a tree-climber, its long tail is not
prehensile. As far as is known, the
childhood of tree kangaroos follows the
same pattern as for other kangaroos,
although it would be interesting to
know more about a baby tree kangaroo's
first excursions out of the pouch.

The Monkey Family

The monkeys and apes are our nearest relations and we turn to them when we want to study the evolution of Man. The five kinds of ape differ from the monkeys in having a more upright stance, broader chest and shoulders, and no tail. Man is a special kind of ape, most closely related to the chimpanzee and gorilla and more distantly to the orang-utan and the gibbons.

Because monkeys and apes are so similar to us, we find their behaviour particularly endearing. The universal appeal of a baby animal with its soft, rounded features is far greater in monkeys and apes because they look so like a comical human baby. The mother gorilla (above) is the epitome of ugliness, yet the infant clasped to her breast in such a human fashion has a definite charm, while the baby orang-utan on page 53 is quite irresistible.

Monkeys and apes give birth to a single baby or sometimes twins. As is so often the case in mammals, the father plays no part in rearing the baby, but all males in the group are tolerant of infants. They do not mind babies playing with them and will come to their aid when danger threatens. The newborn baby is completely dependent upon its mother for food, warmth and protection, because, like the human baby, a primate baby is absolutely helpless. For the first months of its life it must be carried all the time, like this chimpanzee (left). Later it learns to walk about and explore, and even play with other babies, but it returns to its mother when the animals are going to move any distance.

The mother gives her baby more than food and physical protection. She also gives it a feeling of security which comes from the prolonged close contact between mother and baby; without this contact the baby would not develop properly. The same sort of contact is necessary to human babies.

47

The first monkey-like animals were small shrew-like creatures which lived in trees and ate insects. From these animals came first the lemurs, tarsiers and lorises and then the monkeys and apes.

The slow loris (far right, top) is an example of a primitive primate. It lives in South-East Asia, sleeping by day rolled in a ball and climbing through the trees at night in search of fruit, insects and the occasional small bird or mammal. Slow lorises breed at any time of the year and usually have a single baby. The baby loris is already well covered with a coat of fuzzy hair and quite alert, but it still needs to be carried by its mother, first under her belly and later on her back. Sometimes she leaves it clinging tightly to a branch while she goes foraging.

The more familiar monkeys belong on the family tree between the primitive lorises and the advanced apes. Unlike lorises, they are mainly active by day and rely on eyesight rather than smell. Good binocular vision is essential for swinging through the trees, a method of progress called brachiation.

The De Brazza guenon (far right, bottom) is one of a family of monkeys which live in Africa. This baby shows the beginnings of the beard that will be a characteristic when it is adult. Its colouring is, however, different from that of the adult, which is greyish with an orange rump, chestnut forehead stripe and a white beard. The colour changes at maturity, which is unusual because other kinds of guenon change when still infants. Most guenons go around in troops but the De Brazza guenon lives in family parties and does not mix with other monkeys. For the first few weeks of life, the baby guenon lives upside down clasped to its mother's belly. Although still small, this baby is quite old and can already climb about on its own.

The macaques are another group of Old World monkeys which range from Japan to North Africa (the Barbary 'ape' of Gibraltar is a short-tailed macaque from across the Straits). The species shown here (right) is the crab-eating monkey of South-East Asia. This picture was taken in a Hindu temple on the island of Bali, where monkeys are sacred religious animals and are allowed to wander unmolested. Baby macaques are born with a sparse covering of black hair, mainly on the head and back, and are quite different in appearance from the adults, as the picture shows.

After clinging to its mother's breast for some time, the baby moves to her back before leaving her to play with other baby monkeys. From studies of captive macaques, it is obvious that playing with other monkeys is a very important part of a monkey's education. During play, it not only acquires tree-climbing skills, it also learns its 'manners' in dealing with other monkeys and becomes fitted to take its place in

48

monkey society. Some monkeys have overpossessive mothers who will not let them out of their reach and because they do not get the chance to learn, they grow up as social misfits. In turn, they will be bad parents, maybe even abandoning their babies. If all is well, however, the macaque baby enters a friendly world. Adults huddle together sociably and the bond with the mother lasts throughout life.

A move has been made by some monkeys to leave the shelter of the forests to live in the open grasslands. One such species is the baboon (overleaf), a large monkey of the East African plains. Baboons live in large troops in which the males are easily recognized by their large size and the long canine teeth which they use to defend the troop. When the troop is on the move, the mothers and babies walk in the centre with the mature males while younger males form a protective screen around the periphery.

The baby baboon, which is born black, clings tightly to its mother's breast where it becomes the centre of attention. Other baboons like to groom or hold it and its mother is deferred to even by the most senior baboons. Young males sometimes make capital of this by snatching an infant from its mother and carrying it to avert the attentions of aggressive males. Gradually the infant becomes more independent and embarks on its rough educational playing. Its babyish pranks are amiably tolerated by the adults and a baby baboon only has to squeal for the adults to come running to its aid.

The bristly white beard and wrinkled face makes this baby chimpanzee (below) look older than his years, an illusion offset to some extent by his large ears. Baby chimpanzees have a longer childhood than any other animal. Weaning does not take place until the baby is about four years old and it will spend most of its time with its mother for a few years after that. The female may have several children with her at one time, so we can talk of chimpanzee families, although the fathers have nothing to do with bringing up the babies. Something like human affection is exhibited by female chimpanzees towards their offspring. They caress very young babies by lightly stroking them and even kissing them, and adolescent chimpanzees play with their mothers.

When a chimpanzee is born, it is helpless, only capable of clinging to its mother's fur. Its grip is not very secure and its mother gives it extra support by holding it to her breast with one arm and walking doubled up so that the baby rests against her thighs. Support is particularly necessary when the mother is climbing through trees. When about six months old, the baby moves to its mother's back, first clinging 'pick-a-back' then sitting upright, jockey fashion, with feet gripping the mother's flanks and hands holding her hair. It slides back to the protection of her breast when she forces her way through dense vegetation.

By the time the baby is old enough to ride on its mother's back, it is making its first tentative contacts with the outside world. It starts to crawl away and investigate nearby objects or play with its brothers and sisters. At first the mother tries to restrict its movements by hugging it or pulling it back, and for some months the baby will not move more than a few inches from its mother, who is ready to catch it up if it stumbles.

The mother's protection is very important to the baby chimpanzee. It has to be shielded from both a hostile environment and other chimpanzees who may harm it, even if only accidentally. During heavy tropical showers the youngest babies are protected by the mother huddling over them. The baby receives this kind of protection for the first three years of its life and during this period the mother continues to watch its movements carefully, helping it over obstacles and rescuing it if it gets into trouble. If adult chimpanzees approach, the infant is shielded from them. Females continue to protect their offspring until they are well grown. Young male chimpanzees spend an increasingly long time apart from their mothers when they are five or more, but a mother will still come to the aid of her ten-year-old son when he is attacked by mature males, and he will also come to her rescue.

The childhood of chimpanzees has been very well observed because, with patience, it is possible to get the animals used to the presence of human observers. Other species, however, are difficult to study in the wild because they are shy and live in dense woodlands. Second only to the gorilla in size, the orang-utan (right) lives deep in the forests of Borneo and Sumatra, where it cannot easily be observed. Even zoo specimens do not flourish as they are susceptible to infections. This family seems to be a healthy exception, but most of the orang babies born in captivity soon die.

Like the baby chimpanzee, the infant orang holds tight to its mother's fur. Its grip must be very tight because orangs spend most of their time in trees and move from place to place by swinging through the branches. From an early age the mother's milk is supplemented by solid food – leaves and fruit – which she chews first before giving to the baby. By the time it is one year old the baby's weight has increased fivefold and it is searching for its own food. Nevertheless, it stays with its mother for four or five years and even then the bond between them is not completely broken.

A similar pattern of development applies to the baby gorilla (see page 47, right). It grows rapidly and when a few months old begins to supplement its milk with plant food. Young gorillas are weaned at eighteen months and then watch the adults to learn how to prepare leaves, fruits and shoots for eating. Their natural inquisitiveness often leads them to find a new food which the rest of the troop also starts to eat.

Running Babies

In contrast to the baby animals that are born helpless, with their eyes shut and with naked skin, some babies are well developed at birth. After a comparatively long gestation, they come into the world equipped with a coat of hair, their senses alert and their muscles strong. At first they are a little uncoordinated, but after a short interval they are usually able to follow after their mother.

In general, running babies are those whose parents are active, nomadic animals which are constantly on the move and consequently do not build nests for sleeping in. These species are mainly the hoofed animals, which include the even-toed or cloven-hoofed deer, antelopes, camels, pigs, sheep and goats, and the uneven-toed horses and rhinoceroses. In both groups, the majority of species are long-legged runners, like the giraffe (left), and, of great importance from the baby's point of view, they form the major food of many carnivores. The babies therefore cannot afford to be slow and helpless.

Some running babies, for example, baby deer (above), are born in cover and rely at first on immobility and camouflage for safety. A few days later they are brought into the open and are strong enough to run fast. Others, such as some antelopes and horses, can stand within a few minutes or, at the most, an hour, and immediately follow their mothers to mingle with the herd where the concentration of adults acts as a protection against enemies.

For animals whose babies run immediately after they are born, there is a definite advantage if all the births in a herd take place within a short space of time. All the young will then be of the same age and will have the same running ability so that females with offspring naturally keep together.

Open grassland plains are the principal home of baby animals that can run almost as soon as they are born and the savannahs of East Africa are perhaps the best place to find running babies. Interspersed among the acres of grass are scattered trees such as the acacia, which provide both shelter from the sun and food for the long-necked giraffe (right and previous page, left).

Acacia trees are protected by sharp thorns but the giraffes seem unaffected and deftly remove the leaves with their long, prehensile tongues. The males usually inhabit the more wooded parts of the savannah, where there is plenty of food, but the cows and their young tend to stay more in the open. Giraffes are not such good parents as other cloven-hoofed mammals, as they do not keep close contact with their babies.

Giraffe calves are born at any time of the year after a gestation period of fourteen months. Birth is no easy feat as the new baby is already 6 foot (1.8 metres) tall. Its entry into the world is precipitous – the cow delivers it from a standing position and it literally drops into the world. As with other hoofed animals, the forelegs appear first and take the main shock of impact. Within an hour, the calf staggers to its feet and starts to suck. It begins to nibble grass when it is a week old and at four months it is eating leaves like an adult, although it continues to take milk until the age of nine months. During this adolescent period the calf wanders away from its mother and spends time with other giraffes. Some young giraffes have been seen to spend weeks away from their mothers and her milk therefore cannot be a vital part of their diet. The final split with its mother comes when the calf is a year or more old. Fifty per cent of calves die in this first year, and one wonders whether better parental care would save some of them.

Farther out on the plains roam herds of Thomson's gazelles (top left) – 'tommies' for short – one of ten species of gazelle. Tommies are still very abundant on the plains of East Africa. They give birth at any time of the year but more often after the autumn rains. The calf is born in a sheltered place and, although it can stand and suck after a short interval like all hoofed animals, it spends the first few days of life hiding motionless. This behaviour is in contrast to the behaviour of other running babies, such as giraffes and horses, where the babies follow their mothers after birth, but so small an animal as a gazelle would be unable to escape predators by running and hiding is therefore the best defence.

To aid concealment, the female gazelle only visits the calf to suckle it. Three or four visits are made each day and after suckling the gazelle licks up the calf's urine and faeces so that there will be no tell-tale smell to attract

predators. At this early age the calf sits so still that it can be picked up and cuddled without any reaction. A few days later, its behaviour changes and it will flee when disturbed. In spite of these precautions, large numbers of calves are killed, but gazelles are so numerous that it is natural that they should be an important food for the flesh-eaters of the savannah.

The ostrich (far left, bottom) is almost an honorary antelope – it associates with the herds on the plains, where its 8-foot (2.4-metre) height makes it a useful early warning system for the mammals. Ostriches are flightless birds, but as a substitute they are well adapted for running. Only one of the two toes on each foot is used in running – protected by a flat toenail, it is the avian equivalent of a hoof and, aided by their powerful leg muscles, ostriches can attain a speed of up to 40 mph (64.4 k/h).

Ostriches live in groups, a cock accompanied by several hens and young birds. Each hen lays six to eight eggs in a communal nest so that a clutch of up to sixty eggs accumulates. Each egg is 6 inches (152 mm) long and weighs 3 pounds (1.4 kg). These are the largest eggs of any bird, yet at the same time they are the smallest in proportion to the size of the bird.

The eggs are incubated by the cock and one of the hens, the resplendent black cock taking night duty and the drab brown hen sitting by day. Rather than sitting on the eggs to keep them warm the parents shade them from the sun with outstretched wings. Part-way through the incubation period, a strange thing happens – some of the eggs are rolled out of the nest. These were the first eggs to be laid and are therefore at a more advanced stage of development. They are left to incubate slowly in the open and, as a result, all the eggs hatch at the same time.

At first, the chicks are weak but once their plumage has dried they are able to leave the nest and feed themselves. By the time they are one month old they can run as fast as an adult. They are escorted by both parents and if the family group is attacked the chicks run away, then stop and flatten themselves against the ground where their striped patterning and colour make them very inconspicuous. Meanwhile, the parents put their lives at risk by performing a 'distraction' display – they run to and fro, beating their wings and calling to lure the predator from the chicks.

The three animals illustrated on these pages are all antelopes which live in the open woodlands of eastern and southern Africa. The impala (below left) is one of the more common antelopes. Only the males bear horns, and this lamb's hornless head accentuates the size of its ears, showing how it remains alert at all times. The favourite habitat of impala is the edge of woodland, where they can come out to feed on the grasslands and retreat to cover if danger threatens. This is also the baboon's habitat and the two species co-operate, the alert impala giving the alarm and the baboons defending against attack with their long canine teeth. The impala scatter, confusing predators by leaping in all directions, then running together.

Baby impala have to keep up with the fleeing herd because the hunting technique of lions and cheetahs is to single out a straggler. All too often this will be a baby, too young or too bewildered to keep up with the herd.

Impala drop their lambs early in the wet season when there is plenty of succulent grazing for the nursing mothers and for the lamb's first tentative nibbles. In Rhodesia, the first lambs are dropped in early December, each ewe slipping off to give birth alone before returning to the herd with her lamb, but the main lambing period is between December 15 and January 1. The older females give birth first and the two-year olds, giving birth for the first time, drop their lambs later. By February, the baby males are sprouting horns and they are weaned by the time of the rut in late May. When the adults go about the business of mating, the young impala

gather in separate herds.

The gerenuk (below right) lives in dry, acacia woodlands from northern Kenya to Somalia. It is extremely shy and only became known to science in 1878. An apt alternative name is the giraffe-necked antelope. It browses on otherwise inaccessible leaves by standing on its hindlegs and stretching up its long neck. For extra speed, the gerenuk holds its neck low and runs in a crouch. Virtually nothing is known about its breeding habits except what has been gleaned from animals that have been kept in zoos. In the wild, the single baby is born early enough to benefit from the flush of tender shoots that appear when the rains come.

Whereas the gerenuk is able to survive in semi-desert conditions, the waterbuck (bottom right) is more or less tied to riverbanks. It spends the night in the dense strip of woodland that borders the rivers and emerges during the day to feed on the adjoining grasslands. The males parcel out the woodland into territories, but the females live in small groups which join up into groups of about thirty for protection when feeding.

Baby waterbuck are born in the woods and their mothers leave them behind when they go out to feed. So that they leave their babies unprotected for as short a time as possible, females with young leave the woods later in the morning and return earlier in the evening. The youngsters remain in the safety of the woods until they are one month old, when they are developed enough to be brought out into the open to fend for themselves.

The blue wildebeest or brindled gnu (below) is an antelope of open grasslands. It migrates continuously in search of fresh grass and is still very abundant on the plains of East Africa. Nearly 240,000 wildebeest have been counted recently on the Serengeti plains of Tanzania.

Because the herds are continually on the move, travelling as much as 30 miles (48.3 km) a day, baby gnu have to be able to follow their mothers almost immediately after birth. There is virtually no cover where they could hide and the plains are favourite hunting grounds of the big cats. Consequently the calves are on their feet and trotting with the herd within five minutes of birth. The main birth season comes in January and February, the rainy season when the grass is green all over the plains.

Despite their precociousness in learning how to run, many gnu calves lose touch with their mothers and are killed by big cats, hyaenas and hunting dogs. Although adult gnu often form in a circle round calves when a predator is lurking nearby, loss of calves is still extremely heavy. About 80,000 calves are born each year in the Serengeti and this number will be reduced by half during the first few weeks of life.

When the gnus are six or seven months old, danger threatens from another quarter. Rinderpest, a disease of antelope and cattle, strikes the calves and continues to infect them for a year. Known as 'yearling disease', rinderpest kills gnu only during their adolescence. The younger calves are protected by the immunity of the colostrum in their mother's milk and older animals are those whose immunity is acquired from having survived the disease.

The three species of zebra (right) are wild horses which live on the open plains of Africa. There has been some disagreement about the value of their stripes: some people say that they help camouflage, others maintain that the stripes make the zebra highly conspicuous! Certainly, zebra are not easy to see from a distance. Recently it has been proved that zebra recognize each other by the pattern of their stripes.

Zebra do not migrate as much as gnu. Nevertheless, they have to search for water in the dry season and the foals must be active from birth. The mare lies down to give birth and the foal is delivered in about seven minutes. A short while later, it is on its feet, short-bodied and leggy, like the foal of a horse.

Zebra foals depend entirely on being able to run to safety, but the adults also come to their defence and there are stories of bands of lions and human poachers being routed or killed by zebra stallions. The foals are particularly vulnerable in the dry season when their mothers leave them to search for water. This seems callous behaviour on the mother's part but if a mare went thirsty she would be unable to feed her foal and it might die.

The kids of roe deer (left) are among the prettiest of all baby animals, and their charm is enhanced by what appears to be an idyllic family life. Buck and doe spend most of the year together with their family. The buck, however, shows no interest in the kids; he remains there solely for the purpose of mating.

Two kids are usually born to each doe but three is not unusual. They can walk unsteadily after an hour but they stay where they were born, usually in a thicket among tall bracken where the mother lies up during the day. At first there is little contact between the doe and her kids. She spends much of her time away feeding and only returns to suckle them two or three times a day. While waiting, they lie motionless, an easy prey for any fox that sees through the superb camouflage of their spotted coats. If the doe is there she will drive

and are extremely elusive so very little is known about them. In the picture you can clearly see the mobile snout which helps the dik-dik to gather food.

The adults are little larger than a lamb. When alarmed, they run hare-like with erratic leaps through the undergrowth, uttering the two-syllable alarm call from which they get their name, and alerting other animals to the approach of hunters. As dik-diks do not bear a good 'trophy' of horns and their flesh is not even good to eat, they are in little danger from serious hunters.

One function of the 'dik-dik' call is to warn the calves to keep extra still, as baby dik-diks, like roe deer fawns, rely on camouflage for protection. If they are disturbed, they bound away with spectacular leaps that confuse the predator and may give the dik-dik time to escape.

away a fox, attacking it fiercely, but many kids are lost.

One of the pair of kids is usually born stronger than the other and will push forward to take more of the mother's milk. When the pair start to follow their mother, the weaker kid lags behind and may become separated.

A fortnight passes before the doe leads the kids out with her. Tripping carefully through the undergrowth and long grass, the kids gradually learn about their environment by nibbling plants and listening to the sounds of the countryside. Roe deer are surprisingly immune to human interference and may even draw near to watch men at work on forest or farm.

This large-eyed baby dik-dik (above) is one of the smallest antelopes. Dik-diks are found all over Africa south of the Sahara. They live in woods and forests

Domestic Babies

Civilization would not have been possible without domesticated animals. Until the invention of machines, animals were the chief means of transport and labour, as they still are in poorer areas of the world today. They also provide man with meat, skins for clothing and in many treeless places dried dung is used for fuel.

The wide variety of animals which have been domesticated includes elephants, the Tibetan yak, the camel (left) and its South American relative the llama, horses and asses, the cloven-hoofed cattle, sheep and goats, reindeer and even dogs.

Wild animals can be broken or gentled into submission, but it is usually easier and safer to capture baby animals – if young enough, they can be handled safely and they will also imprint on, or form a close bond with, their new guardians. Normally a baby animal imprints on its mother; it stays close to her and recognizes her calls when it is separated from her. But it will accept a substitute mother in the form of a human keeper and can be accustomed to handling so that it remains tame even when it grows up.

The next stage in domestication is to induce the animal to breed in captivity. This is not always straightforward and it could be that ease of breeding was one reason for the choice of the animals we now use. Each generation born in captivity will become progressively more amenable, but even today domestic animals are not necessarily tame at birth. Baby cats and dogs are easy to handle, if only because we start to fondle them before they are strong enough to escape! Baby horses (above) are very different. Within a few hours of birth they can run well; they are wary of anything new and their mothers keep them away from anyone who tries to come close. The confidence of a foal has to be won by a very careful approach, by talking to it and stroking it.

Sheep and goats belong to the family Bovidae which also includes the cattle, buffaloes and antelopes. These animals have hollow horns, unlike the solid antlers of deer, and they ruminate, or 'chew the cud', to make grass digestible. It is not always easy to tell goats and sheep apart, but they can be distinguished by the shape of the horns and by the goat's beard. Male goats have a characteristically pungent smell.

Both sheep and goats lived originally in mountains and high plateaux. Today wild goats still live in Europe and Asia (the Rocky Mountain 'goat' of America is, in fact, a mountain antelope) and wild sheep are found in both the Old and the New World. The North American species are the bighorn, Dall's and Stone's sheep.

Domestication of these animals originated in what is often referred to as the cradle of human civilization, the fertile crescent of Mesopotamia, and bones of domestic goats dated to 6,500 BC have been found at Jericho.

Goats are usually kept for meat, although some are milked. They thrive on very sparse food and will eat almost anything, stripping the countryside – they are an important contributing factor to the barrenness of many Mediterranean countries. Sheep were probably domesticated at the same time as goats and are kept for their wool as well as for meat. The sheep's coat of hair is usually made up of stiff, long guard hairs with a short curly mass of underhairs which help keep it warm. Selective breeding of sheep has gradually removed the guard hairs and developed the underhairs, or wool.

Lambs and kids can stand when they are only half an hour old, and they start to suck their mother's teats two to three hours after birth. Lambs characteristically wag their tails while they are sucking. At first suckling is very frequent, the ewe allowing her lamb or lambs access whenever they demand it. Later the lambs have to seek out their mothers, who limit the time spent suckling by walking away from them.

Even before weaning, the lambs of wild sheep show their independence by forming small lamb herds. The ewes are thus free to graze and may travel many miles from their lambs before returning to feed them. After weaning, the young female lambs stay in their mother's group while the young males leave to join a band of rams until they are old enough to breed.

There are seven races of bighorn sheep living in North America, of which five live in desert regions. The ewe and lambs illustrated (left) are desert

bighorns from Nevada. Bighorns are now extinct over much of their former range in the United States but they survive well in Canada.

The desert bighorns normally breed at any time of the year but in cold climates the breeding season is normally kept short. In the Rocky Mountains, the lambs are born in May. The ewes retreat to remote parts of the mountain slopes where each finds a secluded place among the rocks to give birth. The lamb will be led from this place of safety to the better grazing of the lower, grassy

example, the *merino*, which forms the basis of the wool industry, comes from Spain and has an extended breeding season. In well-managed flocks, mating is controlled so that the lambs are born from February to May and can take advantage of the summer's growth of grass. Suckling lasts for six weeks but, in common with many grazing mammals, the lamb will eat solid food when only a few days old and can eat a little grass by the age of two weeks.

Sheep usually give birth to one or two lambs, but three or four are not

slopes as soon as it is strong enough to keep up with its mother.

The breeding season of domestic sheep (above) can be as varied as the desert bighorns', particularly in breeds that originated in warm countries. For

unusual. There is one record of a litter of eight, but all of them died. In spite of this failure, the policy of sheep-breeding is to increase the number of multiple births as this obviously makes sheep-farming more productive.

Of all the domestic animals, we think of the pig as being raised solely for its meat. It is a surprise, therefore, to find that pigs have been used for pulling carts, as 'hunting dogs' and for treading in seed corn, their sharp hoofs making holes of the right depth for germination.

Two species of pig have been domesticated – the European and the Chinese. They interbreed regularly and some 200 breeds have been produced, including these very odd but rather charming Vietnamese pot-bellied pigs (top right). Also known as hogs or swine, pigs have been domesticated for 5,000 years. They have often been branded as dirty or unclean, but this is rather unfair for pigs are only dirty when kept in the confines of a sty. The prohibition

on eating pigs' flesh probably originally arose from the nomads' contempt for the settled farmers who kept pigs. When they have plenty of room pigs keep themselves clean, although they do like to roll in mud to keep cool.

The European pig (bottom right) is descended from the wild boar which still roams the forests of Europe, where it has a reputation for ferocity. The wild boar looks like a large, rangy, coarse-haired version of a domestic pig. Its snout has the typical mobile, disc-shaped snout that gives pigs most of their undoubted, if somewhat unusual, appeal. The upper canines turn upwards and outwards and are honed against the lower teeth to make devastatingly razor-sharp tusks.

These young wild boars out feeding with their mother (below) were born in the spring. Their pale striped coats contrast with the uniform colouring of the adult and are characteristic of wild pigs. Baby domestic pigs do not have stripes. These piglets are two weeks old and are already learning to forage, although they still rely on their mother's milk. The food of wild boars is mainly leaves, with berries, acorns and roots, but they also eat worms, insects and other small animals.

The wild boar has a litter of five to eight piglets whereas a domestic pig usually has up to twelve piglets which is one reason for its popularity as a farm animal. The record for one litter is an incredible 34 piglets. Pigs are also

popular because they feed on kitchen scraps, and in the fairly recent past a backyard pig was a common sight.

Before giving birth, the sow makes a nest. In natural conditions she roots and scratches soil and plants into a pile, then clears away the centre to make a shallow bowl in which to lie comfortably. If she is confined to a bare concrete sty, she still chooses one particular corner as a nest. The process of birth, technically known as farrowing, takes several hours and if the sow is nervous she may trample some of the piglets. When all of the babies are finally born she uses her snout to draw them towards her udder to feed.

The piglets start to make suckling movements as soon as they are born, even while still attached to the umbilical cord. When they start to suck they embark on the first struggle of their lives. They jostle for position on the udder and within a few days a definite order has been formed, each piglet having its own teat to which it goes every feeding time. The teats at the head end of the sow produce more milk than those lower down the body, so there is competition to be near the head; if there are fewer piglets than teats, the lower teats are unused and regress. The first teat usually goes to the piglet that was heaviest at birth, and as it gets more milk than its brothers and sisters its advantage over them continues. The struggle for position can be quite vicious as the piglets are born with 'milk tusks' which are quite sharp and are used for biting and slashing. Once the teat order has been settled, however, the aggression dies down and the family live peacefully.

While they are still very young, the piglets fall asleep as soon as they have finished feeding and lie neatly lined up along the warmth of the sow's body. When they are older she gets up when they have finished feeding and leaves them in the nest.

Apart from the danger of trampling the piglets when they are very small, the sow is a good mother. When disturbed she gives nasal whistles of warning to the piglets, who immediately crouch motionless while their mother goes to investigate the cause of disturbance. If there is danger, the sow either attacks or tries to lure the intruder away from the nest.

At about the age of one week, the sow leads the piglets from the nest by coaxing them with the same quiet grunts that she gives when about to nurse them. From then on the piglets are ready to start a more independent life, exploring their surroundings, playing together, and learning how to search out and root for their own food.

Domestic animals which are used mainly for carrying or pulling loads are called 'beasts of burden'. Agriculture would have been impossible without horses, camels or oxen to draw the ploughs, and the history of warfare has been moulded by the use of horses. Consequently many societies have placed great commercial value on these animals and have lavished great care on them, particularly on their breeding and rearing.

In the Old World the camel (see page 64) has made it possible for man to live in the driest areas of the Arabian and Sahara deserts. It survives on the roughest grazing and can go for days without water. Camels give birth to one, occasionally two, calves, which look very like the adult except that they lack a hump and have a soft woolly fleece. White camels like the one shown are particularly highly valued. Like other large running animals, the baby camel can stagger on its spindly legs after a couple of hours and runs well in a day or two. Perhaps because of the scant food supply in the desert, it is dependent on its mother's milk for over a year.

The South American counterpart of the camel is the llama (top right), a humpless camel. It is the domestic descendant of the *guanaco* and was tamed by the Incas 4500 years ago. In contrast to the camel, the llama suckles its calf for only four months, which means it can breed every year.

By far the most important beast of burden is the horse (below right). It is derived from at least four wild forms, among them the extinct tarpan of Eastern Europe and Central Asia. The past importance of horses was well demonstrated by Alexander the Great, who named a city after his horse Bucephalus.

Because they are so highly valued, newborn foals are given almost as much attention as a human baby. It is often helped into the world by Man and its cord is cut and the navel dressed. The foal may even be dried with a towel. It struggles to its feet within an hour and searches for a teat, looking in suitable corners of the mare's body, which often leads it to search at the wrong end! The first feed is vital for all mammals as it contains colostrum, a substance which has many essential vitamins as well as antibodies that help fight infection. At this early age, the young foal is very curious and the mare is continually leading it away from danger. Only later does it develop a fear of new objects.

The donkey (far right) is the poor relation of the horse, although it has been domesticated for longer. It is descended from the wild ass of the Near East and Africa. As well as being a tough but menial beast of burden, donkeys were once prized for the medicinal properties of their milk, which explains why Cleopatra bathed in asses' milk.

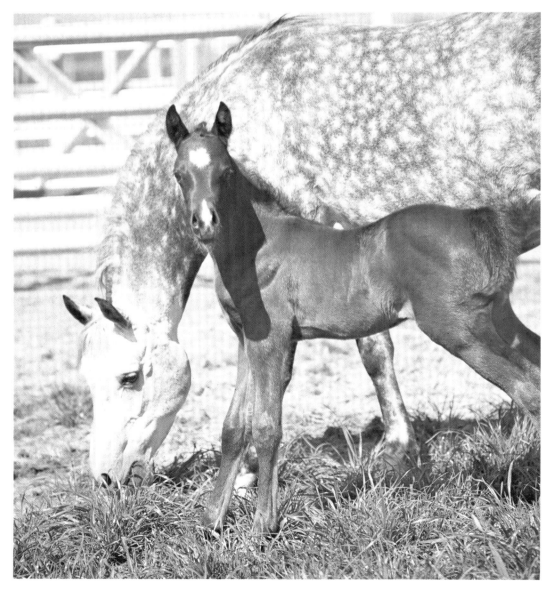

Two kinds of cattle have been domesticated. The European cattle of temperate zones are descended from the aurochs, huge animals which stood 6 feet (1.8 metres) at the shoulder and once roamed the forests of Europe and Asia, while the zebu or humped cattle of Africa and Asia are probably descended from the Malayan banteng. The two kinds have interbred to produce the great variety of modern cattle we know today. You can see the difference between the Jersey cow and calf (above) and the Highland cow and calf (above right). The shaggy coat of the Highland cattle makes it particularly suited to the harsh conditions and poor feeding of winters in the Scottish Highlands.

Wild relatives of domestic cattle include the American bison, the European bison or wisent, the yak, the water buffalo and the African buffalo (bottom right). The African buffalo has the reputation of being one of the most dangerous of all wild animals. It is quite likely that its ferocity has been exaggerated, but the buffalo is clearly no mean antagonist if it is aroused. The calves are considerably less vulnerable than those of the gnu, for instance, as buffaloes have even been seen to fight off attacks by lions.

Breeding takes place at the latter end of the rainy season when the grazing is best. The calves can stand on their feet ten minutes after they are born and

are soon ready to follow the herd.

The origins of domestication are lost in antiquity. The first cattle were probably brought into the service of man over 6,000 years ago in western Asia and by 3,500 years ago several different breeds had been developed. Cattle would have been kept for their meat and milk or as draught animals – there is archaeological evidence for milking and ploughing dating to 4,000 years ago. The economic importance of cattle since these early origins of domestication has been paramount in many cultures. Saxon England and Highland Scotland were dependent on cattle and the long-horned steer was vital to the opening-up of the American West.

However, it is also possible that cattle were originally domesticated for religious rather than economic reasons. Bulls, in particular, were once venerated for their huge size and strength. This is easy to imagine when we think of the 6-foot (1.8-metre) aurochs with its spread of curving horns. Bull cults were certainly important in ancient civilizations, the best known being the Minotaur. Remnants of these cults are still seen in the various forms of bullfighting of south-west Europe. And in Hindu India, cattle are regarded with respect and are strictly protected.

Whatever the reasons for the first domestication of cattle, they certainly lend themselves to taming and

exploitation. Cattle are sociable; they live in herds and readily associate with other animals, including Man. The original aurochs lived over a wide geographical area, and the domesticated varieties are therefore tolerant to widely varying environmental conditions and eat many kinds of plants – stinging nettles included.

The great importance of cattle for agriculture, bullfighting and as draught animals has led to their breeding habits being closely studied. Shortly before giving birth, the cow leaves the herd and wanders off alone. After the calf has been born and the cow has rested, she eats the afterbirth. The calf can climb unsteadily to its feet very quickly and in a few hours it can walk quite well. It takes its first milk within two to five hours of birth. At first, the calf searches for a teat at random and will suck any likely protuberance, but the cow appears to help the calf by nudging it and the calf soon learns the right place.

For the first few days of life, the calf spends most of its time sleeping while its mother grazes. During this period a close bond is formed between the two. The cow identifies the calf mainly by smell and the calf responds to the cow's lowing. Separation causes both mother and calf considerable distress. If the calf is removed altogether, the cow will bellow loudly for several days before settling down, but the calf adapts more quickly and attaches itself readily to other calves or its human owners.

When the cow and calf rejoin the herd, the bond between them keeps them together at first, but gradually the calf starts to wander away and play with other calves, returning only to feed. Eventually it is weaned, the bond with its mother is completely broken and the calf takes its place in the society of the herd.

The keeping of dairy herds has led to a distortion of the normal maternal processes. The cows are turned into milk-producing machines by breeding them for increased yield and a prolonged period of lactation. The records for milk production are held by Friesian cattle – an average yield is 900 gallons (4,091 litres) of milk per year, and the record is 4,280 gallons (19,457 litres).

Outsize Babies

Very large animals often have purely physical problems connected with their unusual size. For land animals, a size limit is imposed by gravity. If elephants got much bigger, they would need such thick legs that they could hardly walk. Sea animals are supported evenly by the water and so do not have this restriction. The blue whale, for example, grows to over 100 feet (30·5 m) long and weighs 100 tons. Although not a true water animal, the hippopotamus (left) has partially solved the problem by spending much of its time in water, which buoys up its massive body.

Outsize babies pose their own special problems. It is an enormous strain on the parents to feed them, so the babies usually grow very slowly and large animals breed infrequently, producing one young every other year at the most.

Sperm whales, for example, can produce only one calf every three years and, like the killer whale (above), bear a single calf after a gestation period of sixteen months.

Blue whales, the largest animals that have ever lived, breed every other year, but this is possible only because the growth of the embryo and baby whale outstrip the growth of every other animal in the world. The baby's express rate of growth is possible because the mother feeds in the cold, rich seas of the polar regions, and can nourish the huge foetus without strain.

For birds, the problems of size are rather different. If they want to fly, their size is restricted by the amount of weight that can be lifted. The 30-pound (13·6-kg) mute swan can only take to the air after a long run, and condors rely on hot-air thermals to keep them airborne. Non-fliers like the running ostriches and swimming penguins are not hampered by weight considerations. Breeding in birds is less of a problem than for mammals because the embryos develop in an egg outside the body and do not have to be carried around.

The warmer parts of Africa and the Orient are the home of a trio of outsize mammals: the elephants, the rhinoceroses and the hippopotamuses – the so-called pachyderms, or thick-skinned quadrupeds. Although they look rather alike with their stout bodies, pillar-like legs and naked skins, the three are not very closely related. The elephants belong to a group of their own, the rhinoceroses are odd-toed hoofed animals related to the horses and the hippopotamuses are even-toed or cloven-hoofed relatives of the pig family.

There are two species of elephant, the African and the Indian. The family life of the African elephant (right) is best known but the two species are very similar. The newborn calf (there may occasionally be twins) weighs 250 pounds (113.4 kg) and stands 3 feet (914 mm) high. There are reports that other females act as 'midwives' when a baby elephant is about to be born. They have been seen disappearing into dense bush with the expectant mother, and later they reappear with the baby. Nobody knows exactly what happens in the privacy of the thicket, and the assisting cows may do no more than stand guard against predators.

The development of the baby elephant is slow and depends on the prevailing ecological conditions. Each cow may give birth once every four years, but when population densities are high the interval is doubled. Under the most favourable conditions, calves may be born less than three years apart. Suckling, too, is variable. It may last for four years but increases to six or more in slow-breeding populations. The mother's teats are located between the forelegs, and her milk becomes increasingly rich as the calf grows in size.

Elephants are solicitous mothers, as shown by this photograph of an elephant in a Ugandan national park which is helping its calf up a steep bank with its versatile trunk. Care for the baby does not end at weaning, nor when the next calf arrives. Instead of driving its calves away, the mother elephant allows them to stay with her until they mature, or even later. The basic unit of elephant society is a female, her youngest mature female offspring and both their current calves. Sometimes these families combine with other parties, to which they will be related in some way, to make a huge 'extended family'.

Because of their vast size, elephants have a problem of overheating. Large animals have a proportionally smaller surface area for losing excess body heat than do small animals, and they are consequently liable to overheat. The African elephant gets around this by using its large ears as radiators. The Indian elephant, which lives in the shade of forests, has not needed to

develop this protection and consequently has much smaller ears.

On the other hand, large size can sometimes be an advantage. Because comparatively little heat is lost, the animal does not have to eat so much to keep warm.

There are two kinds of hippopotamus, the common hippo (see previous page) once found all over Africa and the pygmy hippo of Liberia and Sierra Leone. Hippopotamuses are aquatic (the name means 'water horse') and, like the otter (shown on page 17) all their sense organs are placed along the top of the head so that the animal can see, hear and smell without showing much of its body.

Births occur during the wet season, and in some parts of Africa there are two birth seasons coinciding with the two annual rains. Like the elephant, the expectant hippopotamus leaves the company of the herd to find a sheltered reed bed where she tramples an area to make a nest. The newborn baby is active in a few hours and is brought out to rejoin the herd in its watery home when it is a few weeks old.

While young the calf may lie on its mother's back but it soon becomes an expert swimmer, especially as it has to feed by diving under water to reach her teats. When the mother leaves the nursery area to feed or mate, the calf is cared for by a 'babysitter', one of the

other cows with a young calf. Later, the mother takes the calf on feeding expeditions. It has to walk or swim just beside her and, if it wanders, it is brought to heel with a blow from its mother's head, perhaps rolling it over.

Suckling lasts about a year and a family builds up as the calves spend several years with their mother. They walk and swim in line, youngest behind the cow and eldest bringing up the rear.

The five rhinoceroses of Africa and Asia have suffered badly at the hands of Man. There are barely two dozen Javan rhinoceroses left but black rhinos, shown here (left) basking in the Ngorongoro Crater of the Serengeti, are still quite abundant in the national parks of East Africa.

Rhinoceroses are not as sociable as elephants and hippopotamuses, and when they do form small herds these associations are only temporary. Unsociability is also a feature of their family life. The calf is born, not surprisingly, with no horns but a low stump of horn grows in a few weeks. It accompanies its mother, walking in front of her until the next calf is due two years later. Then the mother drives the calf away, although she may allow it back when the new calf is a few months old.

Among birds the most bizarre example of an outsize baby is the young cuckoo (left). Although it is not outsize in comparison with its true parents, it completely dwarfs the small songbirds on which it is fostered. Rearing such a huge baby is a severe strain, but the baby cuckoo itself makes this easier by ejecting its nestmates and claiming its foster parents' undivided attention.

The female cuckoo sneaks in and lays her egg in a suitable nest when the owners are away. She may remove one of their eggs at the same time. Birds sometimes desert their nests if they find a strange object in them and a high proportion of nests containing cuckoo eggs are abandoned. In many parts of its breeding range, the cuckoo has learnt to lay an egg that resembles closely the eggs of the main host species, so fooling the foster parents and giving it a greater chance of being accepted. This is not the case in the British Isles where the cuckoo has no particular preference and lays its eggs in the nests of a number of hosts.

Once accepted the baby cuckoo is virtually assured of success. It has a shorter incubation period than most birds and therefore hatches before the other eggs. The baby cuckoo then sets about ejecting the other eggs by manoeuvring them into the hollow of its back and heaving them over the side of the nest. This 'murderous' habit has, more than any other aspect of the cuckoo's behaviour, given the species a bad name but, even if the host eggs and nestling were left unmolested, they would surely die. The baby cuckoo grows so rapidly that it would soon starve them out or crush them. It requires so much food that the foster parents have to spend as much time feeding the single baby cuckoo as a nest full of their own young.

At three weeks the baby cuckoo has outgrown the nest and moves to a suitable perch, to beg for food. Its bright red mouth acts as an outsize stimulus for the adult birds to drop food into, so much so that passing birds are diverted to feed the cuckoo in preference to their own nestlings.

Large seabirds such as the gannets and albatrosses lay their eggs in a nest on a clifftop colony numbering hundreds or thousands of pairs of birds. Nine of the thirteen species of albatross live in the southern polar seas where there is a problem of raising the single large nestling during the short summer season. The black-browed albatross (right) nests as early as possible in the spring, as soon as the ice and snow on the cliffs melt and it is able to build its drum-shaped nest. By late summer the young albatross takes to the air and an independent existence. The giant wandering albatross cannot rear its nestling in one summer so it is left on the nest throughout the winter, being fed at intervals, until the following spring.

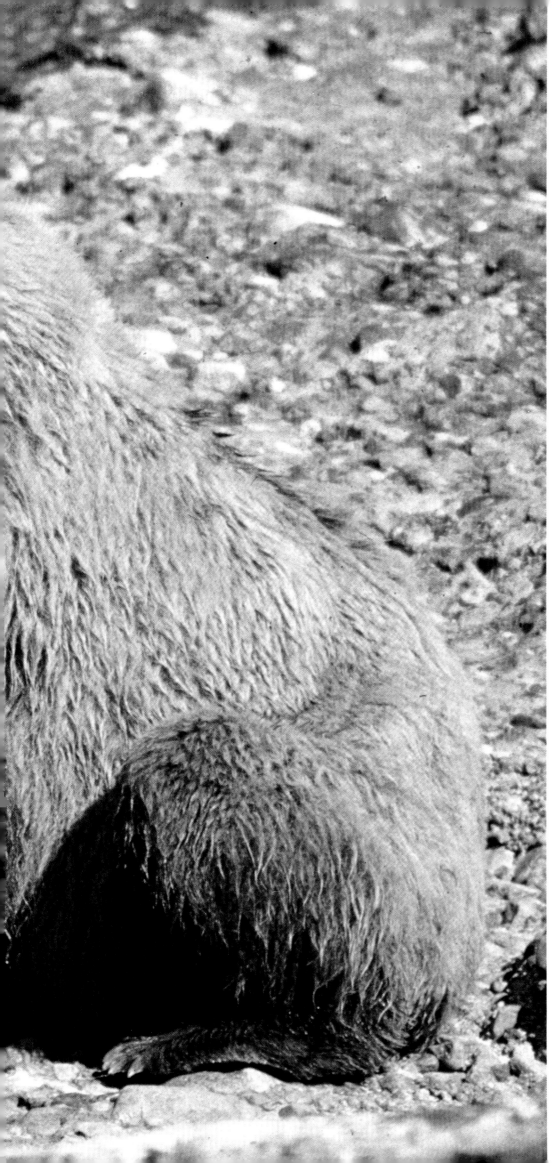

Hunting Babies

Hunting is a specialized way of life. A hunter has to perfect his technique if he is to be successful because his prey is always on the alert for danger. He has to have an intimate knowledge both of the habits of his prey and of his hunting range. Learning how to hunt is a lengthy process and baby hunting animals therefore have a long childhood.

Litters of hunting animals are usually large and the babies are born helpless, like the familiar domestic kittens and puppies. Although many of these animals are now brought up as pets, their ancestors depended on hunting for food and these instincts still survive in them today. The Basset hound (above) was once used on the Continent to hunt everything from deer to wild boar and modern Basset packs still hunt the hare, using their remarkable sense of smell.

The hunters or beasts of prey belong to the order Carnivora and include the cats, dogs, bears, weasels, raccoons, mongooses, civets and their various relatives. The baby bears on the left are Kodiak bears, described on the following pages. Not all members of this order are hunters: the giant panda is well known for eating bamboo shoots, although it does eat mice as well.

The general pattern of parental care in this group of animals is for the mother to be solely responsible for rearing her brood. Usually she constructs a nest in some sort of lair or den. At first the babies are fed on their mother's milk and later she brings food to them. If anything, the young have to be guarded from the adult males, which are quite likely to kill them. There are exceptions to this among the foxes, which are solicitous fathers, and the dog family is, in general, more sociable than other carnivores. In a wolf pack, which is more of a family party than the ravening horde which is popularly supposed to terrorize Arctic travellers, the males bring food to the cubs and protect them while the mother is away.

81

So watchful Bruin forms, with plastic care,
Each growing lump, and brings it to a bear.

So wrote Alexander Pope about the birth of a bear, echoing the strange ideas of mediaeval natural history books, whose authors probably did not see outside their cloisters from one year to another. The general theory was that the bear had a gestation of only thirty days, so short a time that the baby bear was brought forth as a shapeless lump of flesh which had to be licked into shape – hence the common expression. In fact, the gestation of a bear is six to nine months, but the old scholars can be forgiven their mistaken idea because the newborn bear is still wrapped in its birth membranes, which have to be removed by licking. The she-bear licks until the cub is dry and continues to lick at intervals, as will a mother dog or cat.

Another excuse for the error lies in the small size of the newborn cub. It is 9 inches (229 mm) long and weighs only 1 pound (454 grams), 1/350th of the adult weight. It would be natural to expect a larger baby after such a long gestation but the size appears to be an adaptation to the bear's way of life, as we shall see below.

The bear described by mediaeval scholars is the brown bear of Europe, now very rare. Several dozen species of brown bear have been described by zoologists but nowadays experts consider that all are merely members of the same species. The brown bear species includes the grizzly bear of North America, one variety of which is the Kodiak bear (below) which reaches a record weight of 1,650 pounds (748.4 kg).

Mating takes place in midsummer, but development of the embryos does not start until some time after mating – a process called delayed implantation – and the cubs are born in January or February. In midwinter the bears retire to their dens for a long winter sleep, which is not a true hibernation as the physiological body processes do not slow down. As the cubs are born in the middle of the winter sleep, the she-bear cannot release much food reserves to nourish developing embryos and suckle the cubs, so they must remain small. The size of the cubs also makes the birth itself very easy. The mother just rouses herself sufficiently to lick them and move them near her body for warmth and nourishment.

The size of a brown bear's litter depends on the age of the mother. Young bears have single cubs, while those in their prime have two or three. The cubs spend two to three months in the den before their mother leads them into the open. Before then, she will have left them while she goes foraging, but they are much safer when they can follow her, as the den is vulnerable to wolves and other predators. By this time the cubs are beginning to be weaned and they need to supplement

their diet with roots, bulbs and small invertebrate animals.

Although a little shaky at first, the cubs prove to be agile and playful. They can climb trees, a feat rarely performed by adult bears, and even invent a number of new games for themselves – bear cubs have been seen tossing and catching pine cones or rolling head over heels down slopes. Their communal gambols include attempts to trip each other up and wrestling. The first winter is spent in the mother's den and during their second summer the cubs become independent.

The polar bear (right) deserves a position in the chapter on Water Babies because it is a good swimmer, making its home on the floating ice of the Arctic Ocean. At the same time, it is more of a flesh-eater than any other bear. Polar bears range along all the shores of the

Arctic and on the southern fringes of pack ice. They have been seen swimming 200 miles (321.8 km) from land and Nansen, the Norwegian explorer, was pestered by polar bears when he drifted past the North Pole in his ship, the *Fram*. The thick white fur is an adaptation for living on snow and ice, as are the hairy soles of the feet which give a good grip as well as providing insulation. Polar bear fur is good camouflage and Eskimoes used to say that the polar bear covered its black nose with its paw to make its camouflage perfect when stalking seals, its main prey!

Like the brown bear, the polar bear mates in summer and the embryos do not start to develop until autumn, when the pregnant female retires to her den. Polar bears dens have been studied by Russian scientists, who found that the majority are sited some miles inland,

usually on the sides of mountains where there is a good accumulation of snow. The bear digs a tunnel, 2–3 feet (609–914 mm) in diameter and 10 feet (3 metres) deep. The end of the tunnel is widened into an oval sleeping chamber about 4 feet (1.2 metres) high. The walls are well compacted and form a snug hideaway.

The one or two, sometimes three, cubs are born in the middle of winter. Like the brown bear, they are born when very small and have only a sparse covering of hair. Their ears open when they are one month old and their eyes open a week later. The early childhood of polar bears is well known to zoologists and the general public because of the ease with which they breed in captivity. At one time a baby polar bear was a nine-day wonder, with people flocking to see Snow White and Brumas at London Zoo, but now zoo births are commonplace. The pair illustrated here are Sally and her cub Triplet at London Zoo. We know from these zoo births that the cubs start to walk when they are about seven weeks old and are weaned at three months.

Studies of wild polar bears confirm that they emerge from the den in March or later. For a while they return at night or when danger threatens, but as the cubs grow more confident the she-bear reverts to her nomadic way of life, taking the cubs swimming or clambering over ice floes. They stay with her for at least ten months until she drives them away when she is ready to mate again.

The brown bear and polar bear are the best-known members of the bear family, but, from what is known, the habits of other bears are essentially the same.

Some carnivores are not hunters and do not always eat meat. The European badger (above right) and its American cousin are carnivores which have a varied diet. The European badgers eat acorns, berries, fungi, snails, wasps and beetles, which they find by rooting in the soil and undergrowth. They are particularly fond of earthworms. Flesh, in the form of mice and rabbits, is a relatively small part of their diet.

The American badger is a rather solitary animal but the European species lives a communal life in permanent burrows or 'setts'. The babies are born in a nest chamber leading off the burrow system and stay underground for about two months. Their first appearance in the open is very cautious. The sow, their mother, appears first and sniffs the night air. When quite sure that the coast is clear she turns back to the entrance of the sett and coaxes the cubs to follow.

After a week or more the cubs become bolder and start to play. Their games are rough-and-tumble leapfrog or 'king of the castle', and the adults sometimes join in. At this age, the cubs also follow their parents in the search for food.

The slender, agile stoat (below right), also known as the short-tailed weasel, belongs to the same family of mammals as the heavy, bear-like badger. It is a hunter *par excellence* and often catches rabbits and hares which are much larger than itself.

The female stoat makes her nest in a hole in the ground, in a hollow log or under a pile of boulders. Her babies are covered in a fine white fur and the characteristic black tip on the tail only appears when they are three weeks old. They are weaned at five weeks but stay with their mother and hunt in a party.

Young stoats are very playful, twisting and turning together, somersaulting and leaping. But when their adolescence is over, they face the harsh reality of finding a hunting ground and fending for themselves.

The red fox cub (far right) is lucky because its parents will help it to hunt. Its first month is spent in the burrow or 'earth' and the vixen keeps continual watch over her family, leaving the dog fox to bring back food. The first sorties outside the earth are made on quiet evenings. The cubs play together, establishing an order of rank by fighting.

When one of the parents returns to the earth there is a charming greeting ritual. The cubs run out wagging their tails, now thickening into brushes, roll over and lick the parent's snout. The first lesson in hunting consists of the adult holding food in its mouth and avoiding the cubs' lunges as they attempt to seize it. Later, they accompany their parents on hunts and learn how to catch the prey. As the summer passes, the family bonds gradually weaken until adults and cubs are ready to go their own ways.

Although primarily a hunting animal, the domestic dog (right) has been reared as a pet and companion for about 8,000 years, during which time it has been bred into many forms and shapes, many of which are quite unlike the ancestral wolf. The early part of a dog's life has probably been little changed by domestication, despite the revolution in breeding, and the behaviour of young dogs and puppies has been analysed in minute detail.

The pups are born still enclosed by the membranes, which the bitch removes by licking her babies. The licking is also important in stimulating the pups to breathe properly and to crawl in search of her teats. At first the new pups do no more than suck and sleep while the mother keeps them warm and clean. They are almost helpless but if the calm and security of the litter is disturbed, perhaps if the mother accidentally kicks them out of place, they are strong enough to struggle back to safety. A persistent mewing tells the mother if something is wrong. She helps them back into position and the pups naturally scramble towards the warmth of her body. When she leaves the litter to feed, the pups crawl into a pile and so help to keep each other warm.

Three weeks pass before the pups can stand and follow their mother on unsteady legs. This follows a sudden spurt of development in which the eyes and ears start to work and muscles become co-ordinated. Temperature regulation is now working properly and the pups sleep in a row rather than a heap.

As soon as the pups are physically capable of co-ordinated movement, they start to play with each other. Their games include elements of the serious business of adult life, such as hunting, fighting and even sex. Whether they are seriously practising particular patterns of behaviour in readiness for later use or are merely indulging in the only activities of which a dog is capable is a moot point. Whatever the reason for their play, the pups certainly learn to co-ordinate both their own bodies and their relations with their fellows. The first games consist of biting and mouthing each other, and the pups learn how much pain they can inflict on each other without causing distress. A week or two later, they playfully hunt and 'kill' each other by grabbing the scruff of another puppy's neck and shaking it.

Social behaviour makes its appearance in such reactions as a pup guarding a toy against its litter mates, or the litter retreating together when disturbed, each pup following the example of the others. Facial expressions and sounds are important in communicating moods and intentions to other dogs—five-week-old pups learn to express their feelings by movements of the ears and lips, and they gradually increase their repertoire of

growls and whines.

Weaning is accomplished at the age of about two months, by which time the pups are equipped with all the basics of dog behaviour although they continue to improve their skill in physical activities and etiquette until they enter the full social life of adult dogs at puberty.

It is quite likely that the early life of other hunting animals follows the same pattern as in dogs, but training in social behaviour is less important in the more solitary species. Adult raccoons (above left) live independent lives, each occupying its own territory, and the male does nothing to help rear the family. The litter of up to six cubs are born in a tree nest. At birth they are very small and they do not emerge into the open until they are seven weeks old. Their first trips outside the nest are short and they do not start to forage for another eleven weeks. In all, they stay with their mother for a year. Such a long period of dependence may be to give them time to learn all the many different hunting techniques they will need in later life.

Raccoons are very adaptable, and they have survived the destruction of their original woodland homes by moving to towns where they scavenge in dustbins. Their food includes worms, insects, frogs, the eggs and chicks of ground-nesting birds, as well as some nuts and berries. They also search for crayfish and other

animals in shallow water, like the family shown here. There is quite a variety of food open to them, but they have to learn where and when each item is available.

To find its food, the raccoon makes use of its dextrous forepaws which are almost as nimble as human hands. This feature is shared by the suricate or meerkat (above right), a mongoose of South Africa. Like other mongooses, suricates are sociable and live in colonies of about two dozen individuals. As with most sociable animals, for example the monkeys, the male suricates are not completely indifferent to their young. The male helps to groom the kittens but feeding is the responsibility of the mother. She takes the kittens on foraging expeditions and teaches them what is good to eat by laying food in front of them.

Big Cats and Little Cats

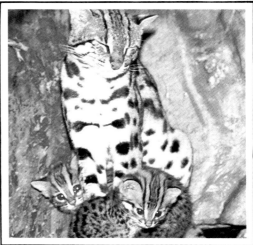

For the pet owner, the most significant difference between cats and dogs is that cats are largely solitary animals. Dogs live in a pack and a domestic dog needs the company of its human companions, but the cat walks by itself. These traits are revealed in the family life of the two animals. In the dog family, the father often helps rear the puppies, but male cats usually show no interest in their offspring and may even kill them if given the chance. The solitary nature of cats is, however, often overstated. Domestic cats are sometimes very sociable and several wild cats live in pairs or small groups, culminating in the family life of the lion which lives in 'prides' consisting of up to fifty individuals.

The cat family numbers thirty-five species, of which all but nine are about the same size and shape as the domestic cat. The smaller cats are rarely seen and their solitary, nocturnal habits make them difficult to study. They include the European wild cat which is now confined to highland areas and the African bush cat, from which the Ancient Egyptians bred the first domestic cats. The leopard cat (above) is a native of South-East Asia. Although the adult is white with a reddish-brown tinge on the back and splashes of black, the kittens look very much like domestic tabby kittens.

Of the nine remaining cats, five are often classed as the 'big cats'. These are the lion, tiger, leopard, snow leopard and jaguar. They sit with their forelegs outstretched, like the Sphinx, whereas the small cats lie with forelegs curled round. The big cats communicate by roaring, but the smaller cats, including the wild cat, lynx and ocelot, purr.

The cheetah (left) is an unusual cat altogether. Built for speed, it has hard, dog-like pads on the feet and, unlike most cats, it cannot retract its claws. It has a small head, with the eyes set high for peering over cover.

The cat is a symbol of comfort and contentment, as is amply demonstrated by this ginger kitten (above). This kitten will soon be independent of its mother. Its early life is very much like that of the pups described on page 86. After being cleaned of its birth membrane, it scrambles towards the warmth of its mother's belly to find a teat to suck. This becomes the centre of its existence for about four weeks, but during the second month of life the kitten starts to take solid food. It will still suckle when it can, searching out its mother and making her lie down, but she becomes increasingly adverse to feeding her kittens and will climb out of their way.

Meanwhile the kittens play together. They indulge in mock fights, dancing sideways at each other with back arched and tail erected into a 'bottlebrush'. The fight may end with the kittens rolling over together while they rake with their claws and bite each other in a simulated fight. Among domestic cats, the family ties are not always completely broken and the cats will live happily together.

Outside the domestic world life is harder for cats, as it is for all animals. An additional trial for wild cats is that they are hunted either for their fur or because they kill domestic animals. The tiger (top right) has been particularly hard hit and it is a good thing that these largest of cats breed well in captivity. Although connected in the imagination with the jungles of India, tigers originated in Siberia. Siberian tigers like this zoo cub have paler coats than the Bengal tigers of India. Their origin in the cooler climate of Siberia is shown

by their intolerance of heat. The Bengal tiger also prefers the shade of forests and lies up during the heat of the day.

The infancy of tiger cubs is prolonged and the tigress mates only once every three years. The litter of two to six cubs are blind at birth, but they already have their distinctively striped coats. Although they are weaned at six weeks, they spend up to two years with their mother. They start to make their first kills at the age of seven months and thereafter the family hunts together, the cubs learning the tricks of the trade from their mother. During this period the tigress becomes more sociable; when they have no family, two tigresses may fight when they meet, but family parties have been seen sharing the same prey without any apparent aggression. Even adult males may be tolerated nearby.

All is not sweetness in the family life, however. Of the half dozen cubs that may comprise a litter at birth, it is rare for more than two to survive to adulthood. The weakest are eaten by their mother.

The cheetah (bottom right) is the fastest land animal. One was recorded with a stopwatch as attaining 71 mph (114.3 k/h) over 700 yards (640 metres) Its hard paws and long legs help give it its turn of speed, and it tends to run down its prey rather than lie in ambush and pounce like other cats. The cheetah is less solitary than most of the cats and troops of cheetahs are sometimes seen, particularly where other big predators are rare. However, the female still has to rear her young without any assistance from the male.

Cheetahs have no particular breeding

season and the two to four cubs arrive at any time. The female has to combine guard duties with hunting, a task which is made easier if there is game passing within a short distance of the nursery. Where families have been watched in the wild, the female has always kept within sight of the nest, although her sharp eyesight gives her plenty of scope as predators cannot approach undetected on the open plains.

Cheetah cubs are distinguished by a straggling mane of grey hair on their necks and, to begin with, they are greyish on the back and dark brown on the belly, which gives them a strange appearance. When they first start to stray from the nest their mother picks them up by the scruff of the neck and carries them back. Later, when they are about two months old and have adult coloration except for the greyish mane, their mother leads them out to play in the open. Unlike the adults, cheetah cubs have sharp retractile claws and are good climbers. A growl from the mother warns them to lie quietly if she spots prey. The cubs watch intently as she makes a careful approach, and then dashes in with a final sprint.

A few months later the cubs will start to hunt for themselves, but their task is made easier by their mother's assistance. In the few observations that have been made, it seems that the adult heads off the prey's escape so that the cubs are given a chance to make the kill. One family of cheetahs was observed stalking a family of warthogs. When they were within 20 yards (18.3 metres) the adult sprinted after the mother warthog while her cubs chased the piglets, the cheetah positioning herself between the adult warthog and piglets so they could not join up. Fortunately for the piglets their evasive behaviour was more advanced than the cubs' hunting behaviour and in this case, at least, they escaped.

The tiger and cheetah have their
moments of sociability but the lion (see
previous page) is the only truly sociable
cat. It lives in 'prides', which are groups
of four to thirty lions, sometimes more.
Each pride contains a number of lionesses,
their cubs and one or more males. The
lionesses do most of the hunting but
the lions drive them off the kill, and
take, literally, 'the lions' share'.

The development of the cubs follows
the general course of other young cats.
They are born fully furred, but marked
with spots which later disappear. They
can see when they are two weeks old and
start hunting at six months, but they
may not become fully independent for
two years.

The lioness gives birth away from the
pride, not so much because she leaves
it, but because the other lions move away
from her. She does not return to the
pride until after five to six weeks when
the cubs are fairly mobile. During this
time the mother has to leave her young
while she hunts for food, and she hides
them in dense cover for protection.
Back in the pride there is safety in
numbers, and the cubs are tolerated by
all members of the group. The cubs greet
their elders by licking their lips and roll
submissively onto their backs to be
licked in turn. Nevertheless, lion cubs
have a precarious existence and many
are killed even before they start an
independent life. Leopards, cheetahs,
hyaenas and even elephants all take their
toll.

After they have joined the pride, the
cubs face an additional source of
danger from strange adult males. If one
of these finds a cub, it will not hesitate
to kill and eat it. Keeping strange
males away from the pride is the task
of the resident males. George Schaller
found that a pride that lost one of its
males also lost 24 out of 26 cubs in two
years, whereas a neighbouring pride
with three males reared twelve out of
twenty cubs over the same length of
time.

Even within the pride, there are forces
at work against the cubs. When a kill
is made, there is an order of precedence
among the lions. The males dominate
at the prey, keeping the lionesses away
until they have had their fill. In turn,
the lionesses drive away their own cubs
by slapping and biting them. This is
surprising behaviour when one
considers how solicitous most animals
are for their offspring. When prey is
scarce the cubs may get very thin and
even die of starvation, so it is likely that
this is a means of regulating the
population according to food supply.
Sometimes, however, the males allow
the cubs to feed with them and so save
their lives.

The bobcat (top) and the ocelot
(bottom left) are American members
of the cat family. Also known as the
bay lynx or wild cat, the bobcat is a
short-haired cat which ranges from

Mexico to southern Canada. It is closely related to the lynx but is smaller, although it is strong enough to attack the occasional cow. Families of kits are born at any time of the year and there may be two litters a year. The kits are born in a den under a log, in a rock cleft or even under a barn or shed. The litter usually consists of two kits, sometimes three or four. Their mother defends them fiercely against owls and foxes, even driving off their father who stays nearby until the kits are weaned. He is then allowed to help bring food to them.

Cats have a traditional dislike of water, but bobcats swim readily and this three-month-old kit is quite at home paddling along with tail held clear. Among domestic cats, the Van cat of Turkey is the only really keen swimmer, but the ocelot is another swimming wild cat, as is the jaguar. The jaguar has to take to the water when its riverside hunting grounds become flooded.

The name 'ocelot' comes from the Mexican word '*tlalocetotl*' meaning field tiger. Its habits are not very well known but it often lives in pairs, the two ocelots keeping in touch by mewing to one another. There is some disagreement about when they breed. Some authorities say that the kittens are born in the winter, while others consider midsummer more likely. It is quite possible that there are sometimes two litters a year and in tropical regions they may breed at any time. There are usually twins, born under a bush, among rocks or in a hollow log and they are fed by both parents.

Although today the Abyssinian cat (bottom right) is a domestic cat, its appearance suggests that it has close links with the wild cats of Africa. It is particularly thought to resemble some of the cats of ancient Egypt, which were venerated as sacred religious animals, symbols of the goddess Bast. The kittens are often born with darker coats than the adults and stripes on their front legs, which gradually disappear as they grow older.

Index

Page numbers in italics refer to illustrations.

Acknowledgments

The publishers would like to thank the following individuals and organizations for their kind permission to reproduce the photographs in this book:

Heather Angel: 12; Animal Graphics: 72; Ardea: endpapers, 4, 17, 22, 23, 26, 26–27, 30 above, 35, 36–37, 39 above, 44 above, 49 above, 50–51, 56 below, 72–73, 75, 88–89, 90–91 above; Douglass Baglin: 42 below, 43; Bruce Coleman: 1, 2–3, 7, 10, 11, 13, 14, 15, 16, 21, 24–25, 28–29, 29, 30 below, 31, 37, 41, 54, 56 above, 57, 59 below, 62–63, 63, 66, 70 above, 72–73 below, 79, 80–81, 81, 82–83 below, 84, 86–87 below, 94 below; Daily Telegraph: 34 below; Ecology Pictures: 18–19 above, 38–39, 94–95 above; Jacana: 44 below, 46, 47, 49 below, 52, 58–59, 59 above, 64, 85, 86 above; Paolo Koch: 76–77 above; Frank Lane: 69 above; Natural Science Photos: 18–19 below, 76–77 below, 90–91 below; NHPA: 9, 32, 32–33, 42 above, 45, 48; Pictor: 40; Picturepoint: 74–75, 92–93; Popperfoto: 6; John Rigby: 71; Spectrum: 65, 90; Tony Stone Assocs: 68; S. A. Thompson: 95 below; ZEFA: 8–9, 19, 20–21, 34 above, 55, 60, 60–61, 67, 69 below, 70 below, 78, 87; Zoological Society of London: 53, 82–83 above, 89.

Case design by Andrew Martin